D1370476

VIRUSES and
the nature of life

VIRUSES
and
the nature
of life

by WENDELL M. STANLEY
and EVANS G. VALENS

Illustrated with photographs, charts and diagrams

E. P. DUTTON & CO., INC. NEW YORK,

Library of Congress Catalog Card Number: 61-5876

Third Printing July 1963

TO NICOTIANA TABACUM

PUBLISHER'S NOTE

WENDELL M. STANLEY succeeded in isolating, purifying and crystallizing a virus in 1935. This was the first convincing evidence that some viruses are molecules similar in some respects to inert substances like sugar or salt. For this accomplishment, which focused the attention of the scientific world on the enigmatic virus, Dr. Stanley received the Nobel Prize in Chemistry in 1946. He is Professor of Biochemistry and Virology at the University of California at Berkeley, founder and Director of the Virus Laboratory there, and Chairman of the University's new Department of Virology. Dr. Stanley is Director-at-Large of the American Cancer Society, past Chairman of the Board of Scientific Counselors of the National Cancer Institute, and a member of the World Health Organization's Expert Advisory Committee on Virus Diseases. He was awarded the Presidential Certificate of Merit in 1948 for his development of an effective influenza vaccine.

This book is an outgrowth of a series of eight half-hour films on the subject of viruses made by educational television station KQED in San Francisco in co-operation with the University of California. The film series was produced for the National Educational Television and Radio Center under a grant to the University from the National Science Foundation. It was directed and produced by Evans G. Valens. The series featured Dr. Stanley and six members of the Virus Laboratory's Senior Staff.

The authors are indebted to the entire staff of the Virus Laboratory. They wish to express their appreciation particularly to Joseph A. Toby of the Laboratory staff, to photographer Richard M. Fowler, and to animation cinematographer John M. Davidson.

5

CONTENTS

THE VIRUS is one of the great riddles of biology.

Whether it is "alive" or not is debatable, for it seems to occupy a place midway between the inert chemical molecule and the living organism.

An inactive virus can be seen only with an electron microscope, and then only after it has been "killed." A virus in action cannot be seen at all.

Furthermore, the moment a virus becomes really interesting, the moment it enters a living cell, it ceases to be a virus.

What *is* a virus, then?

About the only definition that *all* scientists will accept is:

> *Something* . . . infectious and extremely small, which has the ability to cause disease in almost all living things, and which can reproduce only within living cells.

Most of the time, a virus is as lifeless as a rock, and it may remain so for years. Yet it may "come to life" at any moment; all it needs is a vulnerable cell to infect. And during infection, it might well breed viruses of a new type which will proceed to kill 20,000,000 men, women and children, a record claimed by an influenza virus in 1918.

The potency of a virus is easily demonstrated in the case of poliomyelitis. One single polio virus particle can infect a human cell and produce in a few hours some 10,000 new polio viruses, each as infective as the original. Yet the individual virus is so small that it takes millions of them crowded together to make a visible speck. The compound polio crystal in this miniature test tube, pictured

in actual size, contains enough viruses to infect everyone in the world with poliomyelitis, if no one were immune.

This fact is not surprising when we consider the size of the virus. Although the individual virus is a great giant among chemical molecules, it would take 1,000,000,000,000,000,000 polio viruses to fill a pingpong ball; and one virus is to 1,000,000,000,000,000,000 viruses as one quarter of a second is to the age of the universe.

Polio and other viruses are responsible for more than half of the infectious illnesses of modern man and for hundreds of diseases in plants and animals, even in germs. In fact, the viral infections of man represent the last great unconquered area of infectious disease. It is no wonder that we commonly think of viruses in terms of disease.

The exciting discoveries in virology, however, go far beyond the understanding and control of virus diseases. They are concerned with understanding the nature of life itself.

The riddles and the mysterious paradoxes that make the virus so difficult to define are the very things that make it invaluable as a source of answers to the fundamental questions of biology. Its intimate involvement with the complex machinery of living cells, plus its own relative simplicity, make the virus a research tool of unprecedented importance. And the unique status of the virus as a kind of "living molecule" has already proved the virus to be a scientific Rosetta stone which is helping us to relate the structure and chemical behavior of inert molecules to the structure and function of living cells.

This, in turn, should greatly improve our understanding of the origin of life on earth, of the line of evolution from mere molecules to living organisms.

The virus is essentially a parasite, able to reproduce itself only within a functioning cell. Once inside the cell, however, it acts as if it were part of the cell's own complement of chromosomes, and it succeeds in tricking the cell into producing new viruses.

For the virologist, the virus thus becomes an espionage agent capable of extracting from the cell information which the cell otherwise would have kept secret from the prying curiosity of man.

The significance of new information about processes occurring in the very heart of the cell is profound enough to justify predictions that would have been labeled visionary a few years ago. As our understanding of the chemical basis of heredity progresses, for example, we may possibly be able to alter the heredity of living organisms by deliberate chemical modification. Presumably, this could mean the ability to repair inherited defects or to encourage the development of qualities such as mental capacity or resistance to disease.

Even the prospect of making viruses to order is no longer unrealistic. We have already learned—in 1960—how to induce deliberately a permanent change in a particular virus, a change in characteristics which is passed on to the descendants of the altered particle. This makes us wonder if we could not learn to manufacture relatively harmless viruses which could crowd out disease-producing viruses of a specific kind, thus halting the progress of disease. There is also some likelihood of creating a virus which would ignore healthy cells but destroy cancerous cells.

Finally, there is the more distant possibility of creating at least a very simple living organism from scratch, from laboratory chemicals.

Such prospects, of course, imply great benefit to mankind. They also imply potentially grave problems if new discoveries are not used wisely.

In a more general way, the study of viruses has led to some sobering insights concerning the fantastic subtlety of natural biological events. We have gained new respect for the rare occurrence in nature, and we have come to appreciate how profound may be the results of the smallest conceivable chemical change.

We speak of the "rare" sugars, ribose and deoxyribose, or of the relatively "rare" element, phosphorus; yet we discovered not so long ago that more than 6,000 phosphorus atoms and the same number of one or the other sugar molecules are present in and essential to the reproductive mechanism of every virus and of every living cell.

To take another example, we have learned that a particular error in the reproduction of a virus—an extremely rare event statistically—may prove to be a fatal error for millions of human beings.

As to the importance of small chemical changes, we recently came to realize that a slight change in the structure of a molecule may make the difference between skin and fingernails. More startling is the discovery that the difference between a mild virus and a killer could be due to no more than the replacement of three of the 5,250,000 atoms in a single virus molecule.

This is an exceptional possibility, but in principle it suggests the kind of thing we are dealing with when we investigate the chemistry of living things. We hope that ultimately we may be able to describe familiar processes like disease, growth, reproduction and evolution in terms of the changeable arrangement of the atoms that make up all organic molecules.

WHAT IS A VIRUS?

APPEARANCES

WHAT DOES a virus look like?

This is the easiest question you can ask a virologist, for he can show you the pictures.

Viruses are perfectly visible to the naked eye if you have enough of them—a few million millions, perhaps—and if your sample is free of everything but viruses. The viruses then will fit together snugly in a regular geometric pattern. Such a three-dimensional pattern of very small identical units is, of course, what makes a crystal. The herringbone pattern in the crystal opposite is typical of the tobacco mosaic virus.

Poliomyelitis viruses crystallize beautifully, as we can see if we take one of the dozen or so individual crystals from the compound crystal shown on page 9 and place it under an ordinary microscope.

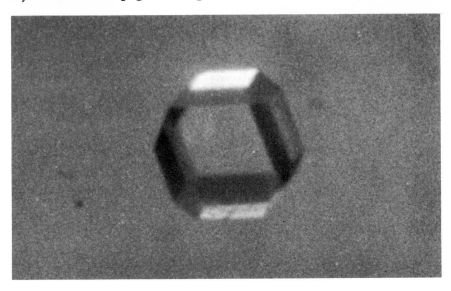

If we slice this crystal in two and look at the resulting cross section in an electron microscope, the individual viruses appear lined up in perfect order. The magnification here is about 150,000 diameters, and this is about as far as we can go. We can enlarge the *picture* as much as we wish, but this will not make the details any clearer; it will only enlarge their fuzziness.

To get still closer to an individual polio virus particle, we have to become very indirect about it. By combining information from such procedures as X-ray diffraction and ultracentrifugation, we can design a model of what the single polio virus particle *might* look like if there were some way of seeing it clearly.

We know there are 60 units of protein, roughly spherical, around the outside of the virus. These are arranged to form 12 pentagons

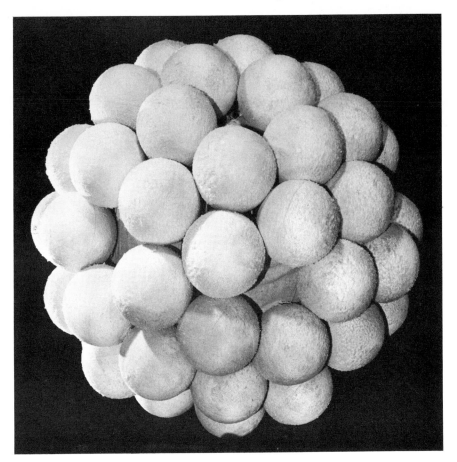

and a large number of equilateral triangles. The protein, which is chemically related to the familiar protein of egg white or gelatin, occurs as balls of long, twisted strands.

The spherical viruses are more common than viruses of other shapes. But we do not know that all spherical viruses are built like polio, for very few viruses have been examined so closely and carefully.

Viruses also appear in the shape of tadpoles (the relatively sophisticated bacterial viruses), as long rods (tobacco mosaic) and big loaves (vaccinia), and in the form of an icosahedron, a regular solid with 20 triangular faces (the remarkable insect virus, Tipula iridescent).

The idealized shapes of these cardboard models are not always obvious in the real thing, as the electron micrographs on the opposite page clearly show.

All these viruses are magnified 42,000 diameters.

The length of one micron, commonly abbreviated as the Greek letter μ, is shown in figure 8. A micron is one millionth of a meter.

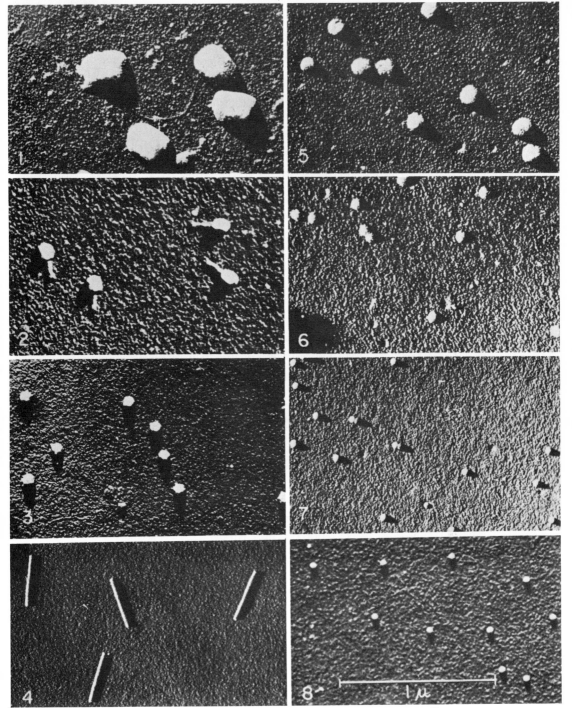

1. Vaccinia
2. T2 phage
3. T3 phage
4. Tobacco mosaic
5. Influenza
6. Papilloma
7. Bushy stunt
8. Polio

Scientists use units of measurement appropriate to the size of whatever they are working with, and most of them prefer the metric system. Just as the meter (39.37 inches) is a convenient unit for labeling track events, the millimeter is a convenient measure for camera lenses, the micron for living cells and the millimicron for viruses.

How big is a millimicron? A millimicron is to a meter as three seconds is to a century. There are 1,000 millimicrons (mμ) in a micron (μ); 1,000,000 of them in a millimeter (mm); and 1,000,000,000 of them in a meter (m). Typical dimensions in the world of the virus, in terms of millimicrons, might run something like this:

9,000——small animal cell
600——wavelength of yellow light
60——average virus
4——average viral protein subunit
.1—likely distance between atoms in a protein molecule

It pays to remember that magnification is commonly expressed in linear terms, which can be misleading. For example, a line of 50,000 tobacco mosaic viruses laid end to end would extend about half an inch, the length of the photographic image of one tobacco mosaic virus, or TMV, on the preceding page. But the line would be far too thin to be visible; 50,000 times as many viruses, or 2,500,000,000 of them, would be needed to cover the entire photographic image. In terms of volume and weight, the electron micrograph shows a virus particle enlarged 125,000,000,000,000 times.

There is a better way than arithmetic to show how small a virus really is in comparison with familiar objects. We can take a tobacco leaf infected with tobacco mosaic viruses and approach it by degrees, coming closer and closer with the help of both light microscope and electron microscope.

In the following photographs we see a tobacco leaf with the fine hairs which give the leaf its velvet touch. Then we see individual hairs, each composed of several hair cells. Occasionally we may find a crystal of tobacco mosaic virus embedded in one of these hair cells. If the crystal is painstakingly removed from the hair cell and dissolved in distilled water, the neatly ordered viruses that make up the crystal will break rank and scatter as individual virus particles.

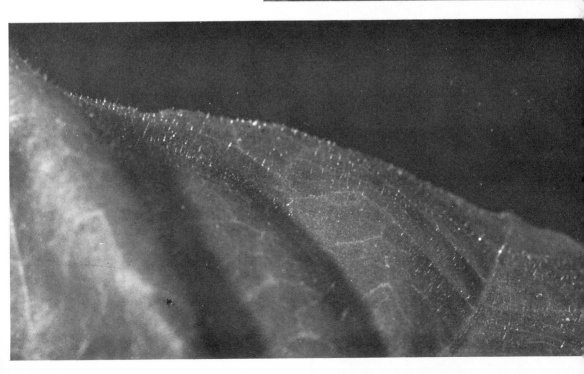

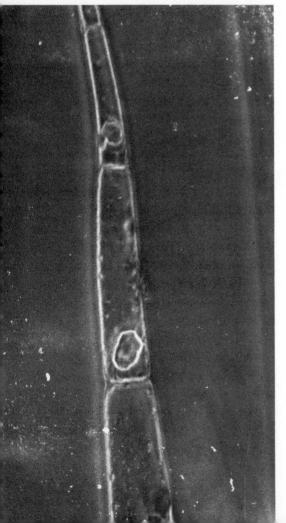

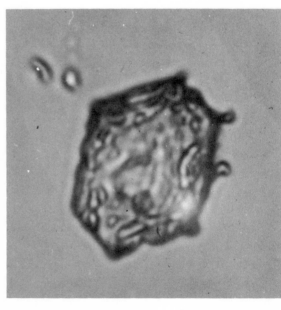

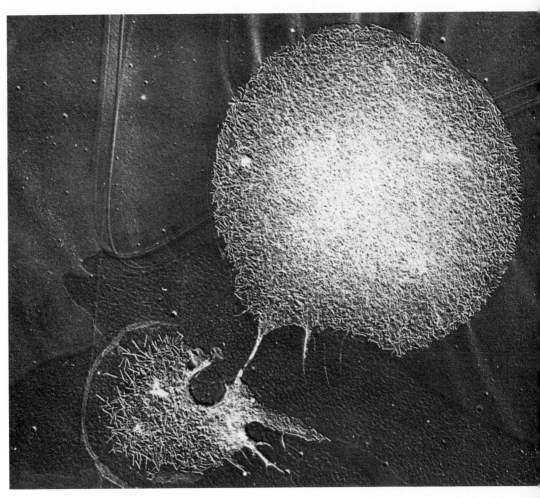

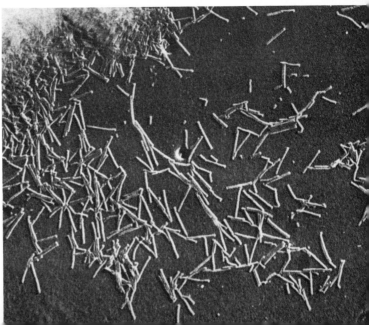

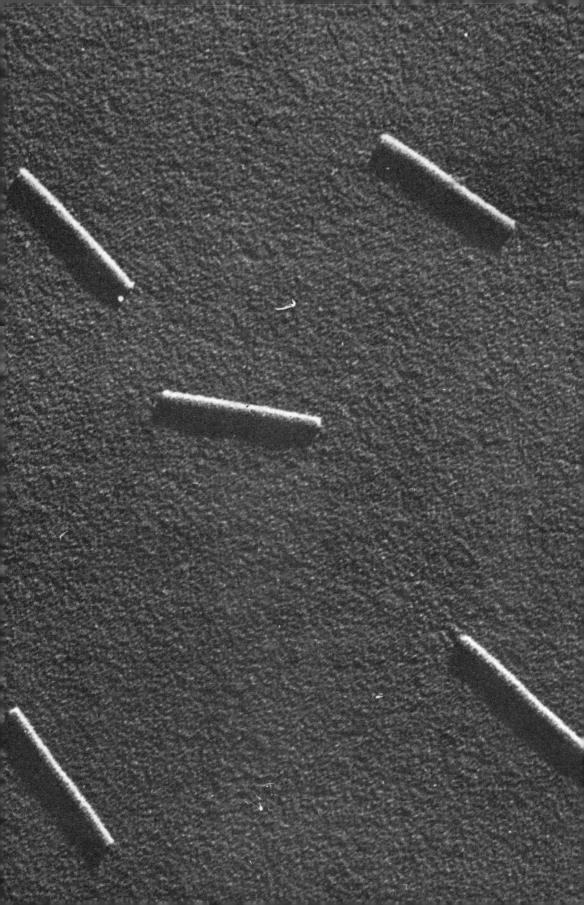

The final picture is an electron micrograph of five of the billions of tobacco mosaic virus particles which made up the original crystal. Each particle measures 18 x 300 millimicrons.

These dimensions nearly bracket the size range of all viruses, for there are no known viruses smaller than 16 or larger than 300 millimicrons. Such specific limits to the size which a virus may assume are neither accidental nor incidental. A certain minimum degree of complexity and a certain minimum number of constituent atoms are required for the self-duplication of any molecule or organism, and 18 millimicrons is close to this minimum. On the other hand, anything much larger than 300 millimicrons will lose the stark biological simplicity which is the mark of a virus.

The size of the viruses is even more significant in terms of the progress of science.

In the late 19th century, living organisms could be found of any and every size between the smallest bacterium and the largest blue whale. Chemical molecules of every size from complex proteins down to the two-atom molecule of hydrogen gas were known. But between the two, between the biologist's living organisms and the chemist's inert molecules, there was a great gap.

Nothing alive could be smaller than the tiny pleuropneumonia organism measuring some 150 millimicrons. No known chemical molecule was larger than about 22 millimicrons. The world of the biologist and the world of the chemist were neatly separated.

But in 1898, an "organism" smaller than any known form of life was discovered, something which could reproduce itself and cause disease in tobacco plants. And in 1935, a molecule larger than any known chemical was isolated and described.

Of course, this "smallest organism" and this "largest molecule" were one and the same: the tobacco mosaic virus. TMV satisfied both definitions in some degree and filled the gap in size between the previously distinct subject matters of biology and chemistry.

Its claim on this twilight zone of life, midway between the living and nonliving, was supported by other viruses discovered during the early decades of this century. These other viruses not only filled the gap in size between organism and molecule, but overlapped at both ends.

WHAT ARE viruses made of?

It took 40 years to find the answer, and the answer was astoundingly simple. Viruses are made essentially of just two substances, protein and nucleic acid.

This conclusion is a long way from Martinus Willem Beijerinck's description of the virus as a "contagious living fluid."

Beijerinck is the Dutch botanist who first recognized the virus as a submicroscopic cause of infectious disease. He also is responsible for giving his discovery the Latin name, *virus,* which means "poison."

In 1898 Beijerinck proved that he could cause disease in tobacco plants by rubbing them with a virus "juice" which had passed through an unglazed porcelain filter fine enough to hold back germs of every kind. His experiment upset the accepted belief that all disease was caused by germs.

Dmitri Iwanowski, a Russian bacteriologist, had performed the same experiment six years earlier, but Iwanowski did not appreciate what he had done; he assumed that his infectious liquid was caused by a defect in his porcelain filter or some poison secreted by germs.

Although the discovery of yellow fever and several other viruses followed the isolation of TMV in quick succession, it was not until 1931 that Beijerinck's "filterable virus" was proved beyond all doubt to be a solid particle rather than a "poisonous fluid."

Four years later, Wendell M. Stanley had a hunch that the tobacco mosaic virus might be a protein molecule, and he ground up a ton of diseased tobacco plants to find out.

The experiment was tedious. It consisted essentially of squeezing the juice from the diseased plants, purifying it, and testing it for possible protein content. In the end, he obtained a single spoonful of microscopic needle-like crystals.

A long series of experiments proved them to be almost all protein and almost all tobacco mosaic virus.

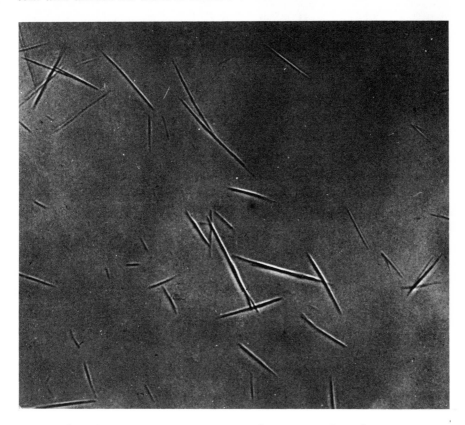

Today the same experiment can be repeated with comparative ease. The juice from diseased plants is decanted, passed through porcelain filters, precipitated and otherwise purified. To the resulting clear liquid is added ammonium sulphate, which will cause protein to precipitate out of a solution.

Something does indeed precipitate, for the clear solution becomes cloudy. When placed under a microscope, a drop of this cloudy liquid reveals a number of slender tobacco mosaic virus crystals.

The bottle labeled "Tob. Mos." contains part of the original solution of TMV crystals isolated in 1935. Each crystal consists of tens of thousands of individual, infectious viruses which, although

bottled up for 25 years, are still capable of causing disease in tobacco plants.

Considerable controversy followed the announcement that the tobacco mosaic virus was a protein and that it could come in the form of crystals. In those days, viruses were thought to be alive, and a "living crystal" seemed unimaginable.

But biochemists throughout the world soon succeeded in crystallizing a number of other viruses, and the dual nature of the virus was eventually established.

In 1937, the British biochemists Frederick C. Bawden and Norman W. Pirie discovered that TMV was not pure protein after all. It was indeed about 95 per cent protein, but the other five per cent was nucleic acid. (The name "nucleic acid" refers simply to the fact that it is an acid first discovered in the nucleus of a living cell.)

The virus was not just a protein but a nucleoprotein—a chemically stable combination of nucleic acid and protein. Nucleoproteins were already known to be present in the nuclei of all living cells.

A simple virus, then, may be defined as a single nucleoprotein molecule. This gigantic molecule is itself formed of a nucleic acid molecule chemically welded to a bulky molecule of protein which forms a protective coating around the nucleic acid.

A molecule, incidentally, is defined as the smallest particle of any substance which can exist free and still exhibit all the chemical properties of that substance. A molecule commonly consists of at least two atoms linked together in a particular way. Many simple molecules may be joined together chemically to form a single large molecule; and a macromolecule containing hundreds of thousands of atoms can usually be analyzed as a sequence of many similar subunits.

The protein coat of TMV, for example, can be broken down into some 2,200 identical submolecules. Each of these smaller molecules, in turn, consists of a long line of roughly similar units. The nucleic acid of viruses is also a chainlike molecule composed of repeated units.

Now, are the ingredients of all viruses the same as the ingredients of the tobacco mosaic virus?

The answer is that all viruses do consist essentially of nucleic acid surrounded by a protein overcoat. But some of the larger viruses may contain small amounts of other materials, and they may have specialized structures such as the tail and tail fibers of bacterial viruses, or the bulky outer membrane of the vaccinia virus. The relatively complex structure of vaccinia, the virus used to vaccinate against smallpox, is rendered visible in these electron micrographs.

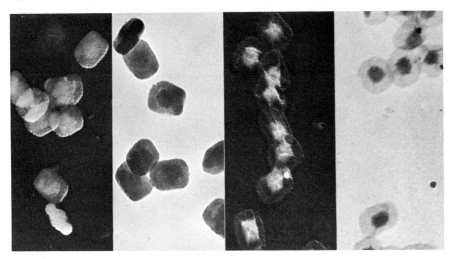

Viruses may differ also in the ratio of protein to nucleic acid or in the kind of nucleic acid they contain.

There are two varieties of nucleic acid: RNA, or ribonucleic acid, which contains a sugar called ribose; and DNA, or deoxyribonucleic acid, which contains the sugar deoxyribose instead of ribose. There are also some differences in structure and in other components.

Many viruses, including polio, influenza and TMV, contain RNA. Others, including all the known bacterial viruses, contain DNA, which is the nucleic acid found in living cells.

How DO we know that viruses exist?

In the light of our present knowledge, this may seem to be a naïve question. But suppose we knew nothing about viruses and only *suspected* that there were such things; what chance would we have of finding one?

In the first place, a virus is invisible. Even a microscope won't overcome this difficulty.

An *electron* microscope might improve our chances, but we still could spend years looking at samples of every conceivable kind of material and not discover a single virus. The electron microscope, after all, is of little use unless the viruses have already been caught and purified.

There is only one way to find a virus, and that is to look in tissues destroyed or damaged by viruses. In other words, viruses are to be found where viruses have already caused disease.

Conversely, disease is the only conclusive proof of the presence of an infective virus.

This fact provides the virologist with an indispensable test which he repeats many times in the course of his experiments. At every step in an experiment he must know whether or not the viruses he is working with are still capable of causing disease. He therefore tries out a small sample of his virus preparation on whatever host the particular virus commonly attacks, be it a tobacco plant, a mouse, a chicken embryo, a colony of bacteria or a culture of isolated human cells growing in a shallow dish. The occurrence of disease symptoms will confirm the presence of active viruses.

The outstanding property of all viruses is that, unlike bacteria, they can reproduce only within living cells. They take over the normal machinery of the cell and convert it to the manufacture of new viruses, which then proceed to infect neighboring cells. The cells are almost always damaged or destroyed in the process, and when enough cells are affected, we see the result as a symptom of whatever disease is involved.

We can say that an invisible virus particle becomes visible by way of its effects in the same manner that we speak of seeing a distant fire when all we really observe is a column of smoke. Where there's mumps, there's virus.

Any one virus is able to infect only a limited variety of cells. This allows us to distinguish three general types of viruses: those which attack plants; those which attack animals, including man; and those which attack the single-celled organisms we call germs or bacteria.

Poliomyelitis, for example, will infect only the cells of man and a few animals. The tobacco mosaic virus will infect only the cells of certain plants. The rabbit papilloma virus is so particular that normally it will infect nothing but certain skin cells of wild cottontail rabbits in midwestern United States.

Closely related viruses, even different strains which appear identical under the electron microscope, are distinguishable from one another by virtue of the specific organisms they are capable of attacking, as well as by the kinds of disease symptoms they produce in identical hosts.

There are a few "good" viruses, by the way, which cause helpful or even beautiful diseases. Myxoma, one of the largest of all viruses, was used with almost frightening success to cut down a destructive plague of wild rabbits in Australia. And there are a few plants, such as tulips, which will develop beautiful colors and patterns when infected with certain virus strains. Such virus-infected tulips have been carefully cultivated for hundreds of years.

Certainly, the bacterial viruses have been model viruses in the full sense of the word. They are convenient and inexpensive to handle in the laboratory, and they have yielded more significant information than any other class of viruses. The one possible exception to this statement is the singular case of TMV, the granddaddy of all viruses. It was the first virus to be discovered, the first to be purified and crystallized, and the first to be taken apart and put back together again. In 1960, it became the first virus to have a specific, laboratory-produced hereditary change built into it by man.

Both TMV and the bacterial viruses have been invaluable in the study of viral growth because they have enabled us to count viruses quickly and directly. Measurement is essential in all scientific investigation, and it is particularly crucial when we have to determine whether a sample of viruses is multiplying and, if so, how quickly.

When a leaf of the tobacco plant *Nicotiana glutinosa* is rubbed with a solution of tobacco mosaic viruses, the resulting disease is localized and individual spots appear on the leaf within a few days.

Each spot is an area of dead cells caused initially by a single TMV particle. Several billion descendants of this one particle have carried the infection to neighboring leaf cells, but the disease is limited to a small area. The number of spots on the leaf is equal to the number of infecting viruses, and from this figure it is possible to estimate rather closely the number of viruses present in the original solution.

Bacterial viruses can be counted in a similar manner and the results are even more reliable. If we have a layer of bacterial cells growing in a round, flat dish and pour over it a solution containing only a hundred or so bacterial viruses, circular spots will soon appear in the carpet of living bacteria. Each spot is a diseased area, a clear area composed of dead cells. It marks the point at which

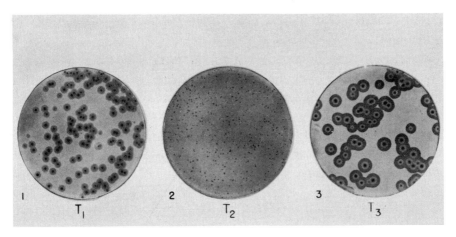

one of the hundred-odd initial viruses came to rest and proceeded to infect a bacterium.

The character of the individual spots, or "plaques," varies according to the kind of bacterial viruses which killed these cells. The three Petri dishes shown here all contain the same kind of bacteria. Each was infected with a different virus, T1, T2, or T3.

Since the T1 and T3 viruses appear to be identical when viewed in the electron microscope, the only way we have of distinguishing one from the other is by comparing the plaques caused by each.

Different kinds of bacterial viruses, incidentally, are named only by letter and number. The letter "T" stands for "type."

An interesting reflection of relative virus dimensions is illustrated by these three bacterial viruses. It so happens that we can determine which virus particle is largest just by glancing at the three plaques.

T2 makes the smallest plaques, and therefore it is the largest of the three.

The reason for this logical, although indirect, conclusion is the following:

To begin with, the bacteria are growing on a jelly surface and are covered by a film of liquid.

Now, limiting our discussion to the growth of only one plaque, we know that the process starts when a single virus infects a bacterial cell. The immediate descendants of this virus infect surrounding cells, and succeeding generations infect still more cells in the vicinity until several billion cells are killed and become visible as a plaque.

Between infections, the viruses in each successive generation are bombarded by molecules in the liquid or in the jelly and thus spread out in all directions from the site of the first infection. The T1 and T3 viruses, being smaller than the T2's, will travel faster and farther as the result of molecular collisions. Hence, the smaller viruses will diffuse more rapidly away from the center of infection and will produce larger plaques.

Dead or Alive?

No ONE worried very much about what it meant to be "alive" before the viruses came along. Animals and plants were alive, minerals were not, and the difference between the two was obvious.

But when the virus was found to occupy some rather vague no-man's-land between the domain of animals and that of minerals, the old philosophical question, "what is life?" gained new significance. And at second glance, it proved to be a profoundly difficult question to answer. The qualities which distinguish the living from the nonliving were not so obvious after all.

What should we name as the most important characteristics of living things? Undoubtedly, we could list hundreds of characteristics, each essential in one way or another. But we should be able to cover most of these by discussing organization, movement, irritability, growth, and reproduction.

Each living thing has a characteristic size and shape, which means that the materials of which it is made are organized in a very specific manner. Since the same basic materials, the same chemical elements, are found in both living and nonliving things, the secret of life must lie in the way in which these elements are organized in vital combinations.

Organization, of course, implies far more than neat patterning or pleasing symmetry. The cells in a honeycomb or the molecules in a crystal are strictly organized, but on a very simple level. In a living cell, the common structural unit of plants and animals, organization involves the specialization of parts which are themselves highly organized.

Furthermore, organization in living things is always dynamic, involving processes as well as structures. The organs of the human body, for example, function to support and maintain one another. The so-called "life process" might be described as a production line running in an endless circle, or in a series of interconnected circles. Each cell in the body is a comparable system of interdependent chemical relationships and reaction chains, constantly in motion.

Movement on a larger scale, that is, gross physical movement, is perhaps the most obvious characteristic of animal life. We immediately recognize a living creature because it wiggles, swims, runs or flies. Even plants can move, although usually their motions are extremely subtle.

Closely related to movement is irritability, or awareness of the environment. This ability to respond to stimuli from outside is certainly peculiar to living organisms. Most plants reach toward sunlight. Ivy twines around a pole, the mimosa leaf closes firmly when touched, and the Venus's-flytrap snaps shut on unsuspecting insects. Cells in both plants and animals respond to the presence of food, some of them actually reaching out to engulf it.

A fourth characteristic which distinguishes the living from the nonliving is growth, which occurs in two ways: by an increase in the number of cells, and by an increase in the size of cells. Cells increase in number by reproducing themselves, and they grow in size by taking in food, from which they gain both energy and raw material. Growth involves metabolism, the process of interchanging material between an organism and its environment; and metabolism is often listed separately as an essential characteristic of life.

Probably the most significant single characteristic of living things is their ability to reproduce themselves and thus create new individuals. In the single-celled bacterium, any reproduction results in new individuals. In the case of complex, many-celled organisms, the reproduction of body cells within particular tissues results only in growth or healing. The union of a sperm with an egg cell is usually required to initiate the development of an entirely new individual. Since all individual organisms eventually die, no form of life could survive without reproduction.

Reproduction implies the possibility of hereditary change, or mutation, the appearance in an individual of some new characteristic which, if not fatal, is then passed on to all his descendants. Mutation is not essential to the survival of all living organisms, but the variety and complexity of life as we know it could never have developed without it.

We might roughly summarize our discussion by saying that the essence of life appears to be the ability to change and to selectively organize simpler units into functioning and relatively self-sufficient wholes.

Now, what about nonliving things, and where do the viruses fit into the picture?

The inanimate world, of course, does not lack everything that the world of the living possesses. Nonliving things often reveal some degree of organization, movement, irritability and growth. Snow crystals exhibit intricate organization in considerable variety. Chemical reactions exhibit a particular kind of irritability or sensitivity. Glaciers, as well as crystals, grow; and many things, from atoms to planets, are in constant motion.

One thing that inanimate objects cannot do, however, is to reproduce themselves. And without reproduction, of course, mutation is not possible.

We begin to see that it is the degree and quality of organization, movement, irritability and growth which distinguishes animal or plant from mineral, not the clear presence or absence of these characteristics.

Only in regard to reproduction and mutation does a perfectly clean statement seem possible: "The capacity for reproduction and mutation is a property possessed only by living things."

But now we come to the viruses, and the statement is immediately open to challenge. For viruses are quite able to reproduce and mutate, and yet they are like perfectly inert matter in other ways.

Viruses seem to be highly organized when compared with ordinary lifeless chemicals, but they are ridiculously simple when compared with the living cell. They are quite like the lifeless chemicals in their inability to move independently, or to grow once they have been assembled.

And, in general, a virus has no way of responding to an outside stimulus. Some viruses do respond to contact with a vulnerable cell by clinging to the cell and eating their way in through the cell wall. But this is essentially a simple chemical response.

Not only does the virus have a dual nature; it expresses one aspect of this nature in one situation and the other aspect in another situation.

On its own, a virus is simply a giant molecule with all the general characteristics of other large molecules. It may exist alone in air or water or earth like a minute particle of dust, or it may be crowded together with billions of other identical viruses in the form of a crystal.

But once inside a cell, the virus attends to nothing but the details of its own reproduction. And in so doing, it manages to come apart and lose completely its own identity as a virus. In fact, its nucleic acid behaves as if it were a functional part of the cell.

In other words, the viruses bear out in both their structure and their behavior the implications of their unique size. They fill the gap between the chemist's molecule and the biologist's organism in almost every way, and they qualify rather well for the facetious labels applied to them by Dr. Thomas Rivers: "organule" and "molechism."

How completely the viruses fill this molecule-to-organism gap was appreciated only after a considerable number of differences *among* the viruses became clear.

The simpler plant viruses like TMV consist of just two parts, a perfectly regular protein coat wrapped around a strand of nucleic acid. Their structure is not too different from that of some of the large, inert macromolecules familiar to the organic chemist.

Bacterial viruses are somewhat more complicated. They have distinct protein "heads," which contain nucleic acid, and narrow "tails." At least some of them also have special protein tail fibers by which they attach themselves to their victims.

The relatively huge smallpox, or vaccinia, virus is still more complex; it seems to have an outer membrane which makes it more nearly like a simple one-celled organism. And it belies our statement that viruses are visible only under an electron microscope, for it is just within the range of the light microscope.

There is still a small gap between the largest virus and the smallest bacterium in terms of structure and function.

This minor gap happens to be filled by a group of microorganisms called Rickettsia, which are carried by ticks, lice and other insects. They are responsible for such diseases as Rocky Mountain spotted fever and epidemic typhus. They were first described by Howard T. Ricketts and Stanislas von Prowazek, both of whom contracted typhus during their investigations and died from it.

The Rickettsia are only about twice as long as the largest viruses. Like viruses, they can multiply only within living cells, although they thrive best on cells which are decadent or dying.

They still resemble bacteria more than they resemble viruses. They are markedly more complex in chemical structure than the viruses, and they have a limited ability to process some simple foods.

Now, it should be clear that the question of whether viruses are "alive" could be argued endlessly without much satisfaction. Viruses resemble living organisms in some ways, they resemble inert chemical molecules in other ways, and they differ among themselves.

But the fact of their in-between nature, plus the fact that they are relatively simple objects that can be studied in detail, has allowed us to investigate certain aspects of living things in comparative isolation for the first time. In particular, it has given us the opportunity to study a chemical molecule capable of duplicating itself. Thus we are slowly coming to understand the chemical nature of the reproductive process as it must occur in all truly living organisms.

In addition, we have gained a new perspective through the study of viruses: instead of seeing the objects in our world as divided into two distinct groups, we now can see a single, continuous sequence of gradually increasing complexity. In terms of structure, we can trace a sequence of closely related objects all the way from the atom, through the simple molecule, the macromolecule, the virus, the bacterium, and the jellyfish, to man. In terms of function, we can trace the uses of energy all the way from the random noise of unrelated molecules to the precise counterpoint of the most subtle biological rhythms.

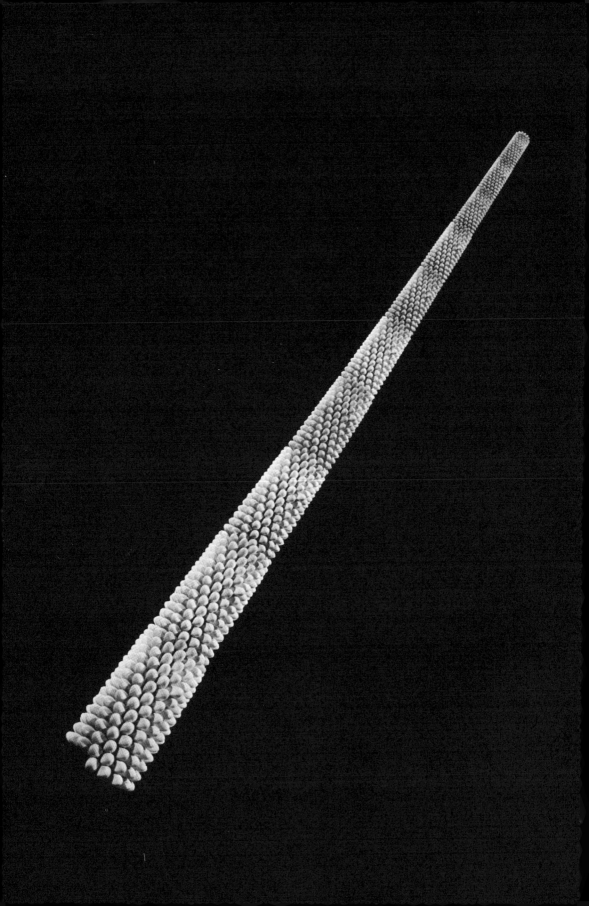

THE VIRUS AS A MOLECULE

ALTHOUGH IT is still something of a feat to discover a new virus, the real challenge is to *describe* what you've discovered. What does this virus look like? What is its shape, its weight? How is it constructed?

There are hundreds of different kinds of viruses, most of them discovered within the past 15 years, and yet no one knows what more than a few of them look like, how much they weigh, or how they are constructed.

The problem is that we cannot even locate an individual virus particle—to say nothing of measuring and weighing it—until we have already isolated many billions of the viruses in a relatively pure sample. Occasionally, viruses are found in the form of pure crystals, but usually they exist scattered wildly among the molecules of many thousands of other substances. We couldn't even describe something as simple as common sugar if sugar molecules were always widely separated from one another.

Once we have a reasonable number of identical viruses separated from everything else, then we can begin to describe them and at the same time make sure that our sample really contains what we think it contains, namely, a virus which will always cause a particular disease in a particular organism under appropriate circumstances.

But so far, only about 20 kinds of viruses have been obtained in pure samples, and only TMV has been described in as much detail as shown in the model on the opposite page. Another 30 or so viruses have been purified to some extent, and all the rest are known only because we can show that a filterable extract from a certain diseased organism will cause the same disease to appear in a healthy organism.

Strictly speaking, everything we shall have to say about the physical characteristics of virus molecules in general applies only to a few dozen specific varieties. We assume that the others will show similar characteristics if and when we are able to purify and study them.

Most viruses, as we know, are inert and unusually stable when they are kept away from the living cells which they normally infect. It is this inactive stage of their existence with which we are concerned when we speak of them primarily as molecules.

But inactivity is not necessarily dull. If a virus had anything to say about the matter, it would surely prefer being called a molecule to being classified as a living organism. Among organisms, a virus is a retarded dwarf and a leeching parasite; among molecules, it is a giant with remarkable properties.

Many of the properties of the inert virus particle could not have been determined at all before about 1940, for a number of the essential measuring devices and techniques have been developed only since that time.

The electron microscope, which operates particularly well in the size range bracketed by the viruses, is barely 21, and the ultracentrifuge is still in its adolescence. Research with the ultracentrifuge, for example, has undergone a period of revolutionary change during the past decade, and the number of ultracentrifuges used to study large molecules has risen from less than two dozen in 1947 to well over 300 today.

The solution of problems involved in measuring, weighing and analyzing something as small as a virus has required also the refinement of techniques borrowed from both physics and chemistry. The physicist tends to look at a virus first of all in terms of its shape and size and weight, while the chemist initially is interested in its composition. And in order to describe a virus molecule in detail, we want to measure it, weigh it and, if possible, look at it; we also want to break it up and analyze the chemical composition of its parts and, if possible, determine the precise manner in which the parts are fitted together.

What we mean by "virus molecule" is not really 100 per cent clear, particularly when we think of the large, complex viruses like smallpox. A molecule may be defined as the smallest piece into which any chemical substance may be broken without losing its identity. For example, a grain of sugar or a drop of water may be divided into billions of individual molecules; but once a single molecule is further divided, it becomes something else. Sugar becomes carbon and water; and water in turn becomes a mixture of gases, oxygen and hydrogen.

Like a molecule of sugar or water, the virus particle is a stable combination of atoms welded together chemically into a single unit; this unit cannot be broken apart in any way and still qualify for the label, "virus."

If a virus happens to have an outer membrane, as may be the case with the smallpox virus, then the particle should properly be defined as a combination of two or more molecules, because the outer membrane and the inner nucleoprotein molecule are probably not a single chemical unit.

Only the simpler viruses such as TMV and polio have been investigated in great detail. The techniques and the results of such investigations are described in the next chapter by Robley C. Williams, a former astronomer who found the electron microscope to be more appealing than the telescope.

Giant Molecules

When a person who works with viruses thinks about a virus, what it means to him may be quite a bit different from what it means to somebody else. This is very much like the situation with a rose. To a rose fancier it is a beautiful flower; to a bee it is a source of nectar; to the small boy it is something that he might get pricked by; to the perfume manufacturer it is a source of aromatic odors. Four or five people or animals, seeing and thinking about the same object, will have different reactions depending upon their type of interest in the object.

Now, I happen to be a person who is mostly interested in thinking of viruses as particles. Such particles, to be sure, are small in comparison to a baseball or a marble, but they are quite large in comparison to an atom or sugar molecule. Particles in this range of size have many of the characteristics of molecules, but they are much bigger than the molecules a chemist ordinarily thinks about. They are called macromolecules or giant molecules.

Viruses can come in quite a range of sizes and shapes, and people like myself are interested in knowing what these sizes and shapes are. And we are interested in finding out whether or not the virus particles have been built with any special underlying architecture. In other words, we should like to know whether they are composed of subunits. And if they are, we want to try to find out as much as possible about the pattern that is used in forming the complete virus particle out of the much smaller subunits.

There is a perfectly good reason for having this type of geometrical curiosity. You might well say that, after we do find out how virus particles are constructed, we know that much—but so what? The answer to this question is involved in the answer to a much broader question that most of us who work with viruses have curiosity about, and that is the question as to how virus particles are put together, or synthesized, within the living cell. On the face of it, all we know is that a virus particle, or perhaps only the nucleic acid of a virus particle, enters a cell; then the cell, if kept alive and in reasonably healthy condition, goes about making many particles of the type that went in.

What happens during this manufacturing process is mostly a mystery, but it is clear that one way of approaching the answer to this mystery is to find out what the finished product looks like. If I were a visitor from Mars and had been instructed to bring back blueprints of one of the large automobile plants, but if I were not allowed to get inside the plant, it would be quite helpful if I could bring back a completed automobile; by studying the way in which the automobile had been put together, I could arrive at a fairly good guess as to how the assembly line had to operate.

And so it is with viruses. After we find out in detail how they are put together, we are more closely able to set limits on our speculations as to how the cell goes about building them. If, for example, we find that all viruses we examine have their nucleic acid on the inside, then we clearly cannot speculate that a virus is built in a cell in such a way as to leave its nucleic acid on the outside of the particle. So people like myself, physical biochemists, electron microscopists, X-ray analysts, and structural chemists, are interested in the shape, size, density, mass, and internal arrangement of these giant molecules. To make this kind of a search we clearly have to use the methods and tools of the physicist as well as, or perhaps more than, the methods of the chemist.

It would be nice if viruses could manage to get outside of cells after they are made, and be in purified form, so that all we would have to do is to take a solution of the material in which, say, a cultured cell is growing and have it contain only virus particles. But the truth is that, even in the most favorable circumstances, the material that comes out of a cell or that we can extract from a cell by our somewhat crude and brutal methods contains virus particles only as a minor fraction. Much cellular debris is extracted also, and the first job in examining the macromolecular characteristics of viruses is to separate the viruses from the unwanted cellular material.

This separation can be done in a fair variety of ways, but one method that is used quite successfully for all viruses, and with particular success for the plant viruses, is a method that involves separation by a centrifugal process.

Let's start at the beginning and go from the plant, which we are going to inoculate with tobacco mosaic virus, clear through the process of purification, until we come out with a solution that contains only water and tobacco mosaic virus particles. In the greenhouse, we inoculate young tobacco plants by rubbing the leaves with an abrasive rod which has been dipped in a solution of TMV.

The inoculation is a very simple process, really, and it is quite

effective since all the plants so rubbed will come down with the disease.

Symptoms begin to appear within a few days. Small veins in the leaves begin to stand out. As the plant continues to grow throughout the week, spots appear on some of the leaves.

Eventually the leaves become mottled, and this tends to show up more clearly in the new leaves at the center of the plant. The mottling usually occurs in a mosaic pattern, which accounts for the name of the virus.

The diseased plants are harvested by simply clipping off the leaves and stems and putting them into a bag. Then we take the bag full of tobacco plants and freeze it, because freezing ruptures the plant cells. The water in the cells freezes into crystals of pretty good size, and these hard, sharp, ice crystals break the cells apart and make extraction of the virus easier.

We put these frozen leaves through a meat grinder, literally, and the grinder finishes the job of breaking up the cells. The material comes out of the grinder with much the consistency of hamburger, since a certain amount of melting takes place.

After we have "hamburgered" up a bucketful of this material, we are ready to extract the juices, which means separating the large bits of cellular debris from the smaller particles, including viruses. We let the material thaw completely and then force it through the pores of a cloth filter by spinning it in a simple centrifugal extractor.

The juice that comes out of the extractor is fairly clear, although it is colored owing to the presence of chlorophyll and some other plant pigments.

Now we have the problem of making a much finer separation of the small particles suspended in the tobacco juice. We have to spin the virus particles out of the fluid, separating them from the water and from the salts and plant pigments.

This is done by using an ultracentrifuge, which acts like a cream separator going at very high speed. However, we are interested not only in what floats on top, as in separating cream, but also in what sediments to the bottom.

So we put the clarified, virus-containing juice in tubes that go into an ultracentrifuge. By spinning it at about 20,000 revolutions per minute for an hour or so, we will sediment to the bottom of the tubes everything as large as or larger than the virus particles. When we take the rotor from the centrifuge and remove one of the tubes, we can see this material as a pellet. Most of the plant pigments and other very small particles are left suspended in the liquid, which we call the supernatant.

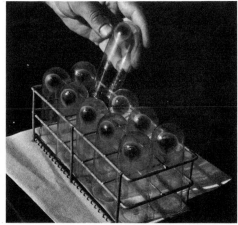

We invert the tubes and discard the supernatant.

We have to go through one more process, because these pellets contain not only virus particles but other, larger particles that happen to be in the solution. So we now dissolve the pellets in water, to which perhaps some salt has been added to help the solubility. We spin this suspension in a centrifuge that goes too slowly to sediment the virus particles. The pellet that we get this time can be thrown away because the virus particles are now left in the supernatant fluid.

We then put this fluid in a centrifuge that will spin at 20,000 revolutions per minute again, and the resulting pellet consists almost entirely of virus particles and nothing else, except water.

The last two processes, repeated two or three times, will give us a preparation which ought to be quite pure.

But virologists are skeptical fellows and would like to have some proof that there are virus particles in this pellet and that there is very little other material.

One way to find such proof is to put some of the virus suspension we have prepared in the electron microscope and take a picture of what's there. As you can see on pages 20 and 21, it is possible to obtain material that is quite pure; you see only virus rods which are typical of tobacco mosaic virus.

We can also follow one procedure of the chemist and find out whether or not the virus preparation is pure enough to allow the particles to crystallize. If there is a lot of contaminating material of different sizes, the viruses won't crystallize.

Actually, when we work with tobacco mosaic virus we won't get fully formed three-dimensional crystals, even at best. We get the needle-like crystals, shown on page 25, which are indicative of high purity.

With some of the spherical viruses like the tomato bushy stunt virus or the polio virus, we can get rather perfectly formed three-dimensional crystals of fairly good size. At least they are of good size to me since they contain several million virus particles, although they are so small that you could just barely see them with the naked eye.

So now we have seen that we can start with a plant or with animal tissue and can extract and purify—and know that we have puri-fied—the particles of many different kinds of viruses.

In some kinds of infections, the amount of virus to be found within the cells is surprisingly large. For example, a fully diseased leaf of a tobacco plant will contain enough tobacco mosaic virus to account for about 10 per cent of its dry weight.

Now comes the problem of characterizing or describing the masses, the sizes, and the shapes of virus particles like those of TMV or polio virus. Clearly, we have to do this before we can look into the question of what, if any, fine-scale substructures these particles might have. There are two general ways in which we can effect this characterization, and whether a person employs one method or the other depends partly on his own preference and partly on the conditions under which he wants to examine the particles.

One general method is to measure the physical properties of the viruses while they are in suspension in water. This method will give an answer, of course, that relates to "wet" viruses; and since viruses normally are made within a medium containing water, it can be strongly argued that we should examine their physical characteristics only when they are in water.

Another general method, which is very powerful because of its direct appeal to the senses, is to take a look at the virus particles with the aid of a microscope, in this case an electron microscope, since the ordinary microscope does not have the useful magnification necessary to do this.

The first method, which we will call the hydrodynamic method, employs an analytical ultracentrifuge, a centrifuge built in such a way that we can measure carefully how fast the virus particles sediment, or settle out of water, in a large centrifugal field.

Particles of different sizes and weights will settle at various speeds. For example, we might experiment with a suspension of rouge, which is a very finely divided iron oxide, and carborundum, a man-made mineral. The particles of carborundum are much larger than the

particles of rouge, and if we stir the two together in a tube of water and then let the suspension stand for a few seconds, the carborundum settles to the bottom. The solution as a whole stays cloudy because of the existence of rouge particles throughout it.

This is a very crude separation, of course, since the particles differ a lot in size, but the force acting on these particles and tending to separate them is only the earth's gravitational field.

Now in a centrifuge we perform the same operation in principle, except that we can use a force ever so much greater than the force of gravity. In fact, with our ultracentrifuge we can apply a force of about 140,000 times gravity or, in astronautical parlance, 140,000 G's. The rate at which particles will sediment in a centrifugal field depends partly upon their weight, or mass, partly upon their buoyancy, and partly upon their frictional resistance.

Frictional resistance is a good indicator of shape. As any fisherman knows, it is easier to pull a bare fishhook rapidly through the water than it is to pull a hook with a fly attached.

And so the shape and size of the sedimenting particles affect how fast they are going to spin down in a centrifugal field. We design our centrifuge in such a way that we can record how fast the particles sediment, in order to make a later analysis.

We start out with a centrifuge rotor into which we can put a small metal cylinder, or cell, containing the virus suspension. The cell has glass on top and bottom so that we can shine light through it while the rotor is turning in the centrifuge.

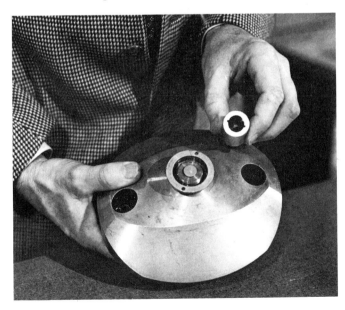

The rotor is put into the centrifuge and attached to the driving mechanism. We start the machine, and when it gets up to about 40,000 revolutions per minute we turn on a light which is fixed beneath the periphery of the rotor. Each time the cell passes over the light, the light shines through the virus suspension inside the cell and is recorded on a photographic film.

Owing to the fact that the solution has optical properties in the region containing viruses which are different from those in a region free of viruses, our photographic record will show how rapidly the virus particles are being thrown to the outside of the rotor cell. In this way we get a permanent record of what we call the sedimentation velocity of the virus.

But now we run into a little difficulty. We don't know to what degree the sedimentation velocity depends upon the size of the virus, and to what degree upon the shape.

Suppose we have two balls of putty of equal size, and suppose we roll one of them out into the form of a long thin stick. Although both are the same weight, the ball will drop through water more rapidly than will the stick, particularly if the stick is falling broadside on. So while we can determine the frictional resistance all right, the answer we get does not tell us whether we had, say, a large particle which was spherical or a small particle which was elongated.

Now we have to look in the catalog and buy another piece of equipment, a viscometer. This is a device which measures how rapidly a liquid containing viruses will pass through a narrow tube; it allows us to distinguish between particles on the basis of their shape without regard to their mass.

When an object is dragged through water, either on the end of a fishing line or by being pulled in a gravitational or centrifugal field, its motion is opposed by forces of viscosity within the liquid. The liquid has to separate, flowing around the object, and come back together again. The molecules of water in contact with the object will move just as fast as it does, but water molecules some distance away will move more slowly. Therefore, the water molecules rub against one another and this effect creates a frictional force which we call the force of viscosity.

This effect can be seen very easily if we compare plain colored water with a solution which contains some particles that are very much elongated, such as the molecules of DNA.

The water, in the right-hand flask, has flowed quickly through a narrow funnel while the solution containing the DNA flows very slowly, just as syrup does on a cold day, and for the very same reason.

 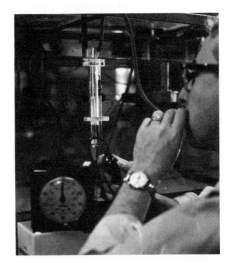

We can refine this simple experiment by using a viscometer. As you might guess from the stop watches, we actually time how long it takes a solution of known concentration to run through a tiny capillary tube in the instrument. The more viscous the suspension, the longer it will take.

By measuring the change in viscosity when we put in higher and higher concentrations of virus particles, we can get a measurement of the frictional resistance; and from this we can estimate the shape of the particles.

Now it turns out that if we put together the information that we have obtained from the centrifuge on how fast the particles sediment with the information we obtained from the viscometer on the frictional resistance of particles, we can come out with a precise determination of the weight of these macromolecules and a fairly good estimation of their shapes and sizes. There is a little uncertainty in the latter figures because our results will depend upon whether the virus particles are swollen or not in solution, and this information is very hard to come by.

Another way of determining sizes, shapes and masses of viruses is to do what I am fond of doing; that is, to photograph the particles after they have been dried and put into an electron microscope. I realize that this is an abnormal environment for viruses, and there is the danger that they won't seem to have the same sizes and shapes when dry as they do when wet. However, there are certain preparative methods, such as freeze-drying, which pretty well eliminate these artifacts.

An electron microscope operates in principle like any microscope except that it uses high-speed electrons instead of light waves. These electrons have waves associated with them, as a matter of fact, but they are so short that the interference effects which limit the power of a light microscope are negligible for electrons.

The electrons are focused by magnets, and the final image can either be seen on a fluorescent screen, as with a television set, or can be photographed.

We prepare our subject for the microscope by spraying a suspension of viruses on a little circle of copper mesh which has been coated with a collodion film and mounted on top of a rubber stopper.

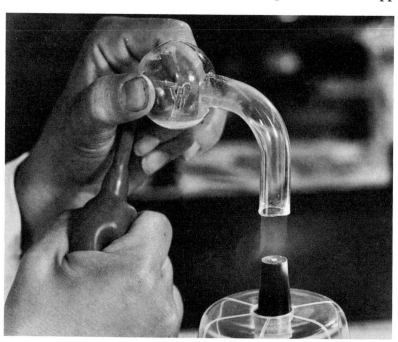

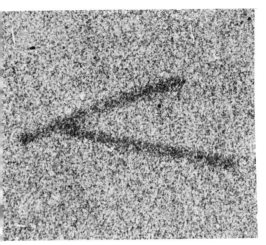 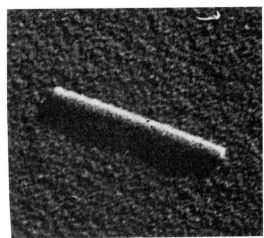

As soon as the spray droplets containing the virus dry out, we have to "shadow" the specimen.

When the electron microscope was first perfected, about 1940, pictures of TMV looked like that of the two particles on the left. An electron micrograph is similar to an X-ray photograph since the beam of electrons in the microscope must pass *through* the subject before reaching the photographic plate. The dark image of the two TMV particles is caused by the fact that most of the electrons striking the particles were scattered and thus never reached the plate.

The resulting dark outline is most helpful in measuring the length and width of viruses, but it gives us no indication of their three-dimensional appearance. We have no clue as to how thick the viruses are, how far they project upward above the collodion surface.

However, if a thin film of a heavy metal such as uranium has been sprayed onto the particles from one side, we get an image like that of the single TMV particle above. This is actually a negative image in which dense areas show up as in the familiar X-ray negative. The white part represents an area where electrons never reached the photographic plate because they were scattered by the relatively thick coating of uranium on one side of the virus particle. There is no uranium at all on the other side of the particle, so the area appears as a black shadow in the final negative print.

The effect of shadowing can be illustrated with a can of white spray-paint and a model of a TMV particle and a polio virus particle.

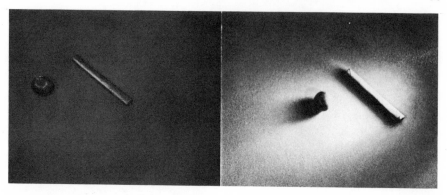

The two models on the left are unshadowed, while the two on the right have been sprayed with paint from one side at a low angle. The difference in visibility is obvious, but the most important thing is that the length and shape of the shadow reveal to us the height and surface irregularities of the models.

To shadow our real virus specimen with a metal film, we fix it to a glass slide in a small vacuum chamber. When a filament of wire is brought to a white-hot temperature, metallic atoms spray outward and strike the specimen at a low angle, depositing a fine film of metal on the near side of whatever may be sticking out from the surface.

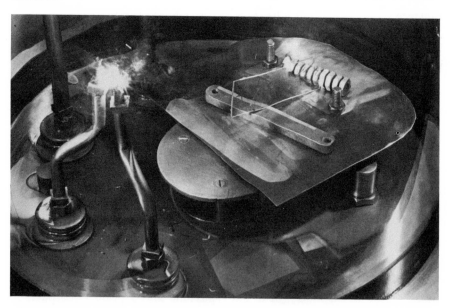

Now we can load the copper mesh containing the shadowed particles into a little holder and insert this holder in the electron microscope. We pump the air out of the microscope to a pretty good vacuum in order to allow the electrons to go down through the instrument from the hot filament at the top without hitting air molecules.

Finally, we turn on the voltage, and the image of the specimen appears on the fluorescent screen. We can focus it by changing the magnetic fields and we can photograph it on ordinary photographic film.

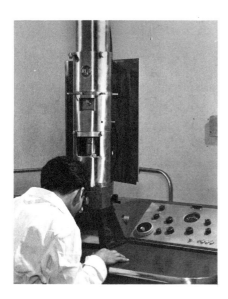 

From the resulting photographs we can determine not only the sizes and shapes of viruses but also their masses. For example, we can take two samples from a virus solution and carefully measure the volume of each. One sample we dry and weigh; the other we place in the electron microscope so that we can count the number of individual virus particles it contains. By comparing the two results we can determine the weight of each particle.

So the electron microscope allows us to measure masses, shapes, sizes and even densities of viruses in a dry form just as the hydrodynamic method gives us these measurements for viruses in solution. Which method gives the more reliable results is constantly a matter of debate, but for the most part the results agree. Since the two methods are quite independent, we can place some confidence in the answers we get.

The agreement of both results, by the way, is an indication that there is not much swelling of the virus particles when they are in a water suspension.

What do we find when we examine the characteristics of virus particles by these physical methods?

We find that for a given virus, such as TMV or polio, the particles are quite uniform in size, shape and molecular weight. But from one kind of virus to another there is great variation. There is a variety of shapes and sizes, as we have already seen; and the masses of different particles range all the way from a molecular weight of about 500,000,000 (which means that the virus molecule weighs about the same as 500,000,000 hydrogen atoms) to less than 5,000,000.

But all this information about shapes, sizes and weights isn't enough. What we want to do is to find out how viruses are put together. And since about 1952 we have made considerable progress.

It is possible to take tobacco mosaic viruses and degrade them gently, and then we see that the nucleic acid of the virus has come apart from the protein. Next to the photograph of an intact virus rod, magnified some 120,000 diameters, is a virus with its protein coating partly removed and its nucleic acid core protruding from both ends. At the right is a tiny doughnut, a section of the protein coat with a hole through its center, seen in cross section. Below is nucleic acid which came out as a very long, fine thread.

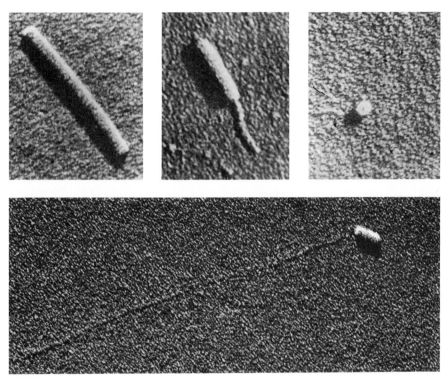

All we have seen, however, is that the nucleic acid and the protein of the virus are separable, and we have seen something about what they look like. But how are they packed together in the virus? What is the fitting arrangement?

To answer this question we have to use X-ray crystallography.

If we take a crystal of viruses and shine X rays through it, we get a geometrical pattern where the X rays have been scattered; and

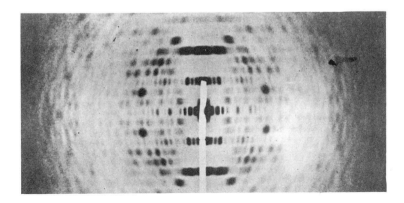

they are scattered in certain definite directions, the directions depending upon the fine structure of the particles that make up the crystal. If the viruses have subunits, the number of these in one virus particle and the way they are fitted together can be deduced by the X-ray crystallographer.

Now what have we learned about the detailed structure of the virus molecule from our recent investigations?

It has been found that most viruses have a highly ordered or patterned arrangement of their component parts. The nucleic acid of the virus, which is a threadlike molecule, is localized near the center of the particle; just *how* it is arranged on the inside is still largely unknown.

Around the outside of the virus there are subunit structures of protein. For a given virus, each of these subunits is the same size. In the spherical viruses, the protein subunits are not simply placed at random over the surface; rather, they form a highly regular pattern.

In the polio virus, each of the protein subunits is arranged like every other one in that each subunit has five close neighbors. The net effect is that the subunits form pentagons, with a total of 12 pentagons accounting for the 60 subunits of the virus particle. This arrangement also causes them to fit in groups of equilateral triangles and in groups of parallelograms.

While the model on page 15 shows the protein subunits as being spherical, we don't really know that much about them. But we do know that there are 60 of them and that each has the same chemical composition, the same size and the same shape, whatever that shape may turn out to be.

Another way to assemble a virus is seen in the model of a tobacco mosaic virus particle on page 38. In the case of TMV, the protein subunits are stacked in a helical or springlike fashion. But each subunit again has the same size and the same shape, and the number of them per turn of the helix is the same no matter where, along the helix, we go.

In the case of a few other viruses, the protein subunits are arranged in a form such that the net effect is to produce a particle having faces that are flat planes and giving to the entire particle an exquisite crystalline shape. A beautiful example of this is the

Tipula iridescent virus, or TIV. This virus is built in the form of an icosahedron.

The way we determined its shape, incidentally, underscores the value of "shadowing." An electron micrograph of TIV seems to tell us only that it appears six-sided. But when a number of shadowed specimens are examined, some shadows prove to be four-sided and pointed while others are five-sided and blunt at the end.

If we take a number of polyhedra made from cardboard and light them from various angles, we soon discover that the only kind of a solid figure with flat sides which will cast both five-sided *and* four-sided shadows is an icosahedron.

We can prove the point by comparing a cardboard model lighted by two lamps 60 degrees apart with an actual TIV particle doubly shadowed in a similar way with a metallic film.

An even more distinctive characteristic of TIV is that pellets of the purified virus have fascinating optical properties. Examined in ordinary reflected white light, the pellets are iridescent, shining with color. Each pellet is a mass of small crystals, and each crystal is oriented in a manner such as to reflect some particular wavelength of the white light which illuminates it. The over-all effect is iridescence—the reflection of light of differing colors from numerous tiny areas.

The jacket of this book is made from a photograph of an array of TIV crystals which, on one rare occasion, was formed on the flat surface of a microscope slide.

We have seen how we can extract virus particles from living cells—in our case, from the cells of diseased tobacco plants—and purify them. And we have seen how a virus can be weighed, measured and photographed, either whole or in fragments. The chemist now is able to break up these fragments into individual subunits and then pull these subunits apart for a still more detailed analysis.

All that we have learned about the structure of viruses is interesting enough in itself, but the real value of these investigations lies in the inferences we shall eventually be able to make about the way in which viruses are actually constructed inside living cells. We cannot study the virus at work inside the cell, and the viruses we *can* get at and dissect are not at work. But the more we learn about the detailed structure of the "idle" virus, the closer we shall come to understanding how this structure comes to be built inside the cell. This, in turn, may make it possible to do something about virus diseases, and it will certainly lead to a better understanding of the vital functions of all living cells.

Robley C. Williams

An Atom's-eye View

IF WE PUT together all the information we have been able to wrest from the virus molecule by one ingenious trick or another, we can construct a reasonably accurate model. We shall use TMV to illustrate this, for the very good reason that more is known about its structure than about the structure of any other virus.

A close look at a model of a single TMV particle gives us a fairly good atom's-eye view of this giant molecule. On the next page is a short section of a tobacco mosaic virus which is lying on its side; the photograph covers about one four-hundredth of the total surface. Spaced with monotonous regularity are the outer ends of seven of the particle's 2,200-odd protein subunits, each of which weighs about 950 times as much as the water molecule in the center of the picture.

The entire virus is both a monster and a rarity among molecules, for most of the individual molecules in the world we live in are comparable in size with those of water. There are, of course, many substances containing molecules as large as TMV subunits and larger, but by far the most numerous of molecules, statistically, are those of rock, water and air. The most abundant compound in the solid crust of the earth is silicon oxide, a molecule which, like water, consists of only three atoms; and the two-atom molecules of nitrogen and of oxygen, plus some water vapor, account for 99 per cent of the air we breathe.

From the point of view of the common two- or three- or four-atom molecule, the virus molecule, with its 5,250,000 atoms, must look something like the photograph on page 38.

The subunits of the virus are set like shallow steps in a great spiral staircase, making some 130 turns around the central nu-

cleic acid core of the particle. The vertical distance between the centers of any two adjacent coils of subunits is about 20 atomic diameters, as we can see from the relative size of the one oxygen and two hydrogen atoms of the water molecule.

Furthermore, each of the 2,200 or so subunits is fitted against six neighboring subunits in precisely the same way, with the exception of those at either end of the virus.

The most striking property of this inert virus molecule is the intricate precision of its architecture, and this observation implies a great deal about the way in which new viruses must be put together inside the cells of a growing tobacco plant.

The protein coat of the virus is not just smeared onto a clump of nucleic acid, as we once imagined it might be. It is fashioned brick by brick in such a deliberate manner that we are led at once to suspect the presence of some kind of master blueprint or template inside the virus-infected cell. And this is precisely what the most recent experiments with TMV appear to confirm, as we shall see when we come to consider the chemistry of reproduction.

All that we have learned about the molecular structure of viruses is the result of a series of discoveries which have appeared at progressively shorter intervals.

In 1898, Beijerinck named the virus and described it as a mysterious something smaller than a germ. In the mid-1930's, the tobacco mosaic virus was found to be a single nucleoprotein molecule that could be crystallized. About 1954, virologists succeeded in analyzing the protein of TMV and determining the relative amounts of the various amino acids of which the protein is made. Soon after that, a comparable analysis was made of the nucleic acid section of the molecule.

In 1960, a listing of the exact sequence of the 158 amino acids in each of TMV's protein subunits was completed, and today virologists are tackling the much more complicated problem of determining the sequence of some 6,500 units which form the nucleic acid core.

When this task is finished, we shall have a record of the blueprint which specifies the kind of viruses to be made within an infected cell. This record should allow us to reconstruct the probable sequence of intracellular events which constitutes reproduction.

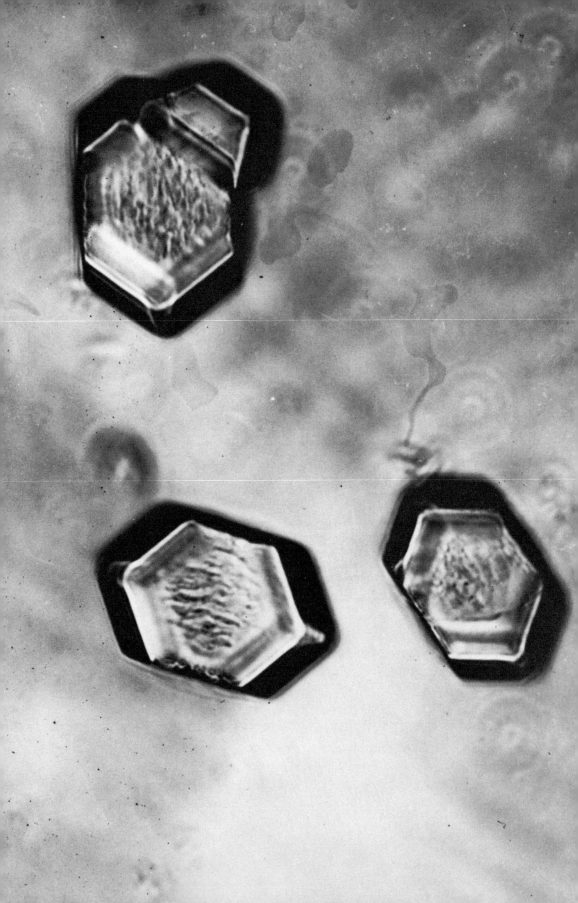

THE VIRUS AS AN ORGANISM

The Dormant Spark of Life

A VIRUS crystal is a gem, albeit microscopic and weighing one two-hundredth of a carat or less. It is rare, very expensive and often quite beautiful (witness the Coxsackie crystals opposite, magnified about 450 diameters, and the Tipula iridescent crystals on the jacket of this book). Such crystals may exist for decades without showing any more signs of life than a diamond. If kept dry, they should last forever.

This sounds like a convincing argument for classifying the virus as a molecule, except for one qualification: "virus" means "poison," and the virus crystal is a *poisonous* gem, capable at any moment of coming to life, of becoming a killer and of producing a billion more crystals as lifeless—to all appearances—as the original.

While the mineral existence of each inert virus molecule in the crystal may go on for years, even centuries, its *active* life is limited to a few hours at most.

It is this one active moment in an otherwise long but static career that we are totally concerned with when we speak of the virus as an organism. For it is during this period, which may be as short as 13 minutes, that the virus displays the two most essential features of all living things: it reproduces itself and, while doing so, becomes liable to permanent, inheritable change, or mutation.

Reproduction, of course, is responsible for the persistence of all life on this planet; and the fact that living creatures mutate, that individuals are occasionally born with some characteristic not inherited from either parent, is the essential fact that made possible the evolution of life as we know it.

The fact that viruses also mutate accounts not only for the likely evolution of viruses from earlier forms but also for the persistence of fatal virus diseases. If viruses never changed, most of their victims would long ago have developed successful defenses against them in the course of their own evolution. But so long as a virus, too, can mutate, it will not necessarily be thwarted by a host organism which becomes immune to it.

For example, a successful influenza vaccine was developed in 1943, but it was utterly useless in the Asian flu epidemic of 1957 and 1958. One or more descendants of the common type A flu virus apparently had undergone a mutation which made it indifferent to the vaccine, and this particular strain therefore thrived and spread throughout the world.

Because of mutation, the characteristics and habits of viruses are constantly changing. New virus strains appear which can infect plants or animals that were previously invulnerable. Other mutant viruses will cause entirely new patterns of disease symptoms in infected organisms, perhaps killing a host that otherwise would have lived, perhaps merely scarring a host that otherwise would have died.

Events such as these serve to underscore the fact that viruses, like all living things, are forever involved in a struggle for survival, forever at the mercy of natural accident, continually dependent upon other organisms and upon their own biological ingenuity.

One intriguing example of this ever-precarious "balance of nature" was discovered in a "species battle" between viruses and bacteria isolated in the artificial world of a glass laboratory dish. The dish contained a large colony of bacteria; the colony, originating from a single bacterium, was supplied with appropriate food. Viruses which commonly infect this type of bacterium were added to the dish, and they soon destroyed nearly all of the bacteria. This was apparently the end of the show, for there was practically nothing left for the viruses to attack. But after a period of time, individual colonies of bacteria appeared and proceeded to grow rapidly, quite indifferent to the billions of viruses that surrounded them. Apparently, a few of the bacterial cells had undergone a beneficial mutation, leaving them immune to the viruses which had destroyed their ancestors.

In a less constricted environment, it is entirely possible that a subsequent mutation might occur among the viruses, resulting in a mutant virus capable of infecting and destroying the new, virus-resistant bacteria. Here we have a fine, though limited, example of how mutation permits evolution and how survival directs its course.

Mutation involves some change in a developing cell or virus, and this change is often caused by natural hazards such as cosmic radiation. Mutation seems to consist of random changes. The great majority of these are undoubtedly destructive or indifferent; the destructive mutations are likely to be lethal and therefore are not passed on to succeeding generations. The indifferent mutations do not affect the survival of the organism in any way.

"Good" mutations are much less probable, but occasionally a mutant form of some organism will find itself better off in a particular environment than its "normal" forebears. This mutant, like the Asian flu virus or like the virus-resistant strain of bacterium in the glass dish, will thrive and reproduce while the old strain tends to die out.

Now some questions we should very much like to answer are these:

What, *precisely*, occurs when a mutant form of any organism is produced? When and where and how is mutation accomplished? Does the event involve a sudden change of structure, and if so, exactly what kind of a change is involved?

The discovery that viruses share with all living organisms the ability to reproduce and mutate, coupled with the fact that viruses can be studied in much greater detail than can living cells, suggested an opportunity to find some of the answers. In fact, this opportunity looked so promising that it led to the development of a new field of scientific investigation: the chemistry and physics of genetics. This new discipline complements the traditional study of genetics; it is concerned with the finely detailed changes which occur when any organism, including the virus, reproduces and mutates.

The primary aim of this investigation is to relate the *processes* of reproduction and mutation to changes in the chemical and physical *structure* of the virus or cell involved.

Experiments such as Dr. Williams described seek first to determine the structure of the virus as a giant molecule and then to speculate as to what functions such a molecule might be capable of. But we also can approach the problem from the other end with genetic experiments, which seek first to determine the genetic functions of the virus or cell and then to consider likely structures which might be responsible for these functions.

Both approaches are essential, and both are possible in the case of the virus. But examination of the fine structure of reproductive mechanisms in the cell is practically out of the question. Consequently, the virus is the one and only "organism" in which both structure and function can be determined and compared. And what we learn from the virus will tell us what to look for in the cells of higher organisms and where to look for it.

If we can integrate what we learn about the structure of viruses with what we learn of their genetic behavior, then the virus will serve as a "model" by means of which we hope to explain the most fundamental process in life, that of replication. This is the process which precedes the division of every living cell, initiates the growth of every new creature conceived, and is the instrument by which evolution has, in a few billion years, fashioned man.

The most co-operative and helpful virus in this search for an explanation of biological replication proves to be the relatively large virus which infects the smallest of all living creatures, the bacterium.

Initially it was thought that this virus somehow breaks into the one-celled bacterium and begins at once to reproduce itself.

Some of the early experiments were designed to determine whether the new viruses were produced all at once or were turned out in succession like automobiles coming off the production line.

What was done, in brief, was to allow viruses to infect the bacteria and then to interrupt at one-minute intervals whatever activity might be going on inside the bacterial cell.

Actually, one infection experiment was halted after the first minute, another experiment after the second minute, and so on. After each step, the infected bacteria were broken open and their contents analyzed to determine the number of infectious viruses present.

It was expected that no more than one virus—the original infecting particle—would be found for each bacterium until at least several minutes had elapsed. Perhaps two or three new viruses per cell would then appear at regular intervals. Or perhaps there would be first two, then four, then eight, then 16 viruses per cell at regular intervals.

The actual results were not exactly in line with the tentative predictions. After the first minute—and after the second and third and fourth minutes, also—there were no infective viruses at all, not even the one-per-cell with which the experiment had begun. Not until after the nineteenth minute did they begin to show up; and yet, by the end of the twenty-fifth minute there were several hundred viruses for every infected bacterial cell.

In the next chapter, Gunther Stent, whose special interest lies in the area of bacterial viruses, discusses this question of how a virus manages to disappear in the process of reproducing itself.

Reproduction and Mutation

Bacterial viruses, that is, viruses which infect, grow on, and kill bacterial germs, were discovered independently in London and Paris during the First World War. These viruses have come to be known as *bacteriophages,* a word derived from the Greek, meaning "eaters of bacteria." They are called "phages" for short.

The discovery of viruses that infect bacteria, themselves the smallest organisms known to man, caused tremendous excitement in the world of medical microbiology, because it was hoped that the killing power of these bacterial viruses could be put to use for the cure, control, and even ultimate eradication of all those bacterial diseases which had been the plague of mankind since the dawn of history.

This idea was not a bad one. Let us take the case of a bacterial disease such as cholera, caused by the cholera germs. It would only be necessary to isolate in nature the virus which infects and kills the cholera bacteria, cultivate this virus in the laboratory, and then disseminate it throughout the world. The anticholera virus should then seek out the cholera bacteria wherever they could be found and destroy them; thus mankind would be rid of the cholera threat.

This hope initiated a tremendous amount of work on bacterial viruses during the 1920's and 1930's, whose goal was making such bacterial virus therapy a practical thing. But, alas, it did not prove possible to cure or control even a single bacterial disease in this clever way. And nowadays, particularly since the Second World War, the fantastic success of antibiotics has made this problem much less acute.

But all this earlier research on bacterial viruses was not wasted after all. For, just at the time when people finally gave up hope that these bacteriophages would ever amount to anything in a practical sort of way, bacterial viruses became one of the foremost tools of *avant garde* biology.

As the fundamental nature of the growth of these viruses was learned, it came to be realized that the bacteriophage could be used as an excellent model system for the study of biological self-reproduction.

Here is something that reproduces its own kind in a simple and dramatic way. A bacterium is infected by a bacterial virus particle. Half an hour later, this bacterium pops open like a burst balloon and liberates into the world about 300 virus particles which are identical with the parent virus. And so the problem we can put to ourselves is this:

What is the trick by which the virus manages to make all these replicas of itself from the hodgepodge of materials at hand? What happens inside the infected bacterial cell during the 30 minutes within which the parent virus managed to give rise to 300 offspring?

Much of the work during the 1940's and 1950's devoted to the study of bacterial virus reproduction was carried out in the hope of

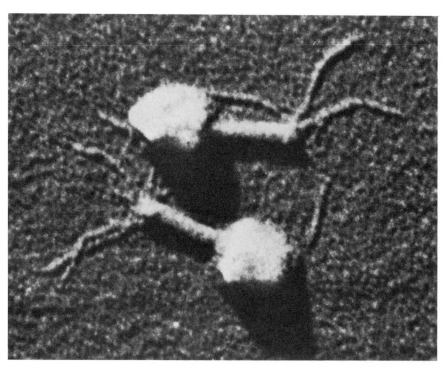

learning something about the details of chemical and physical mechanisms which intervene during these crucial 30 minutes.

This electron micrograph shows what such a bacterial virus looks like. It is a portrait of the bacteriophage T2 which infects the coli bacterium inhabiting the human intestine. The virus is seen to be a tadpole-shaped object with a hexagonal head and a long, hollow tail, at the end of which are several tail fibers. Its over-all length is about one hundred-thousandth of an inch. The tail and the outer shell of the head are made of protein, and inside the head we find deoxyribonucleic acid, or DNA. These materials, protein and DNA, make up practically all of the substance of this virus. There is very little else.

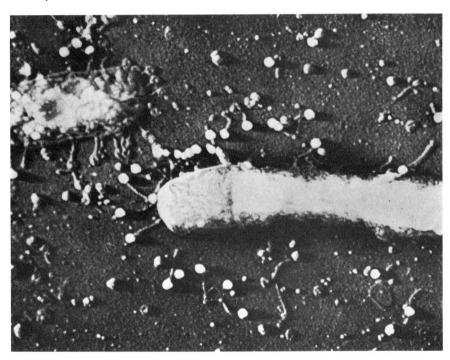

This sausage-shaped object is the coli bacterium, the host organism of the T2 virus. The little tadpoles are the T2 particles. About 1,000 of these viruses would fit into a single bacterial cell.

We are now ready to consider the life cycle of this particular virus, that is to say, the manner in which the T2 virus reproduces itself.

The virus has no means of locomotion, but it is constantly pushed around by the bombardment of the speeding molecules of the liquid in which it is suspended. If the virus thus meanders into the neighborhood of a bacterial cell, it may collide with the cell several times and eventually attach itself to the surface of the cell by means of the tail fibers.

Once the virus is thus anchored to the cell, a strange thing happens. The virus drills a hole through the cell wall, and the tail of the virus particle contracts. The virus particle is now uncorked, and the deoxyribonucleic acid, or DNA, in the head of the virus is injected into the cell, as if the tail were some kind of hypodermic syringe. The protein shell of the head and the protein tail stay outside, although a bit of protein possibly may enter the cell. The job of infection is accomplished once the viral DNA has managed to penetrate into the bacterium.

Once the viral DNA is in the cell, it initiates the drama of self-reproduction. That is to say, the viral DNA now causes the cell to manufacture viruses instead of cellular parts. The raw materials for this process are some of the components of the bacterium as well as sub-

stances taken up from the growth medium after infection.

The viral reproductive process consists of two principal parts. On the one hand, the viral DNA fiber duplicates itself several hundredfold, generating new DNA fibers for the offspring viruses. For this purpose, the original DNA fiber first serves as a *template* for the manufacture of a faithful copy of itself. At this point there are two copies of the viral DNA. Each of these two fibers now makes a copy of itself, producing four copies of the viral DNA. The four copies then double to make eight fibers, and so on, until several hundred fibers are present in the cell.

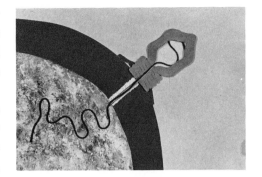

On the other hand, the viral DNA also induces, or presides over, the construction of protein units which will become the heads and tails of new viruses.

Some 10 minutes after the infection starts, the first new DNA fibers begin to combine with the new viral protein to become the first structurally intact virus particles of the offspring generation.

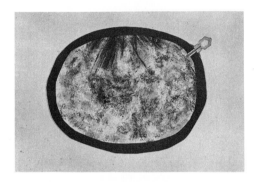

As time progresses, more and more intact, mature new viruses are formed as more and more DNA units combine with more and more protein units, until several hundred offspring virus particles have been constructed inside the bacterial cell.

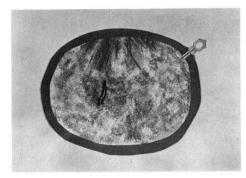

At about the thirtieth minute after infection, some 300 new virus particles are in the cell. The infected cell gives up the ghost, bursts open, and liberates the brood of progeny viruses. Each new virus is ready, willing and able to infect and kill the next bacterial cell it encounters,

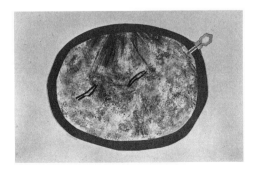

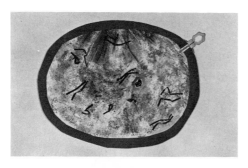

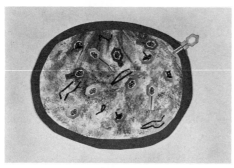

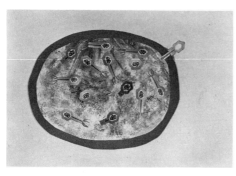

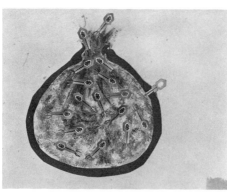

repeating the same reproductive drama.

Now let us consider how one counts the number of bacterial virus particles which may be present in any given preparation, since all exact experimentation depends on having available a reliable *assay* method. Of course, it is possible to place a suspension of bacterial viruses under the electron microscope and count directly the number of virus particles visible. However, this method is not only very cumbersome but also impractical for the type of experiments we shall be concerned with. Fortunately, another assay procedure is available—the so-called "plaque count" method. More than any other factor, it is this excellent and convenient assay method which has contributed to making the bacteriophage the darling of modern biology.

The following operations summarize this method:

We start with a round glass dish, which is filled with agar, a nutrient jelly made from seaweed.

On the surface of this nutrient jelly we place about a million bacteria of the type

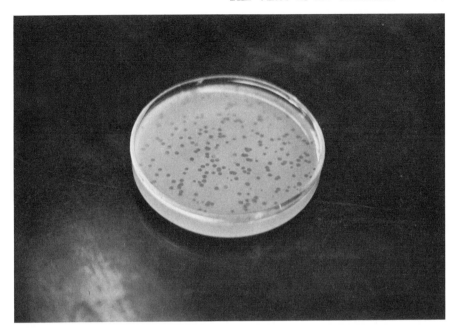

that is sensitive to the action of the virus which we wish to investigate. At the same time we place just a few hundred virus particles on the agar surface. The dish, containing agar, bacteria and viruses, is then placed in an incubator for the night and kept at a temperature— 100° Fahrenheit—which will allow the bacteria to grow.

The next day when we take the dish out of the incubator, we find the agar covered with a turbid layer of bacteria containing a few hundred very distinct holes. What is the meaning of these holes, or *plaques*, as they are called?

Let's consider what happens during incubation. The million bacteria initially put on the agar divide and grow until they cover the jelly surface with a thick carpet of bacterial cells.

Each of the several hundred initial virus particles, however, will find a bacterial cell in its vicinity and infect that cell. Half an hour later, the cell will burst open and liberate some 300 progeny viruses. These 300 new viruses will then infect other bacterial cells in the immediate vicinity and do their dirty work. After another half-hour, a new generation of viruses—by now nearly 100,000— is released from the 300 newly killed cells to further spread the slaughter of neighboring bacterial cells.

Consequently, holes begin to develop in the bacterial carpet. These holes, or plaques, which are masses of destroyed cells, grow in size until they measure up to an eighth of an inch in diameter. Each plaque then marks the spot where an initial virus particle came to rest on the jelly surface the night before. The plaque is an area of the bacterial carpet where, instead of living bacteria, there are millions of virus particles, all descendants of that original great-great-grandparental virus.

Since every virus particle is capable of initiating the growth of such a plaque, the number of holes, or plaques, in the bacterial carpet is equal to the number of virus particles originally placed on the jelly surface. Hence a count of the number of plaques reveals to us the number of viruses in the sample to be assayed.

Now, when we look at thousands of such plaques, as every good bacterial virus worker does every day, we find from time to time an unusual or variant plaque, which looks different from the rest.

In this dish, for example, all of the plaques are clear, and

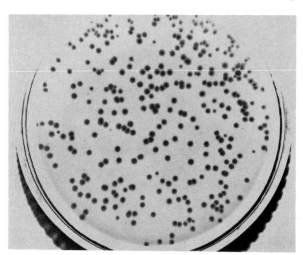

through them you can see the black paper underneath the Petri dish. But one plaque, high on the right, is different from all the rest; it is larger than the others. We call it a large, clear plaque, in contrast to all the small, clear plaques surrounding it.

If we pick up this large, clear plaque out of the agar and replate the virus colony contained in this unusual plaque, we find that all of the bacteriophages present in this plaque now produce the variant large, clear plaque type.

This finding means that the initial virus particle which caused the first large, clear plaque must have been a hereditary variant, or *mutant.* Some characteristic of the original virus has been suddenly changed, a characteristic which determines the way in which the virus will reproduce in, and kill, the host bacterium, with the ultimate result that the plaque formed by the mutant virus is large and clear instead of small and clear.

Our mutant virus, furthermore, is a *stable* hereditary variant, since it passes on its newly acquired characteristic to all of its offspring.

This seems to be organic evolution in action. We have seen that the bacterial virus, T2, produces many billions of exact replicas. But we have also seen that once in a while, perhaps once in 10,000 or so times, an *in*exact or faulty replica is made. This "imperfect off-spring" is a mutant, and it will pass its particular imperfection on to its own descendants.

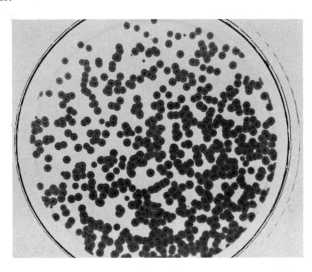

But how does the change occur? What causes the mutation? Mutants must arise as "copy errors" during the reproductive process.

We shall have to examine once more the role that the viral DNA plays in the reproductive process. When a virus infects a bacterium, the viral DNA is the only component of the virus to enter the bacterial cell. Therefore, it must be the DNA which carries into the cell all the information needed to cause the death of the bacterium and the production of several hundred new viruses. DNA must be the carrier of all hereditary information; it must be the substance which determines whether the new viruses to be made inside the cell will make large plaques or small ones.

DNA, then, must be intimately involved in the process of mutation. But in what way?

We can picture the DNA of the original virus particle as a very long, ladder-like molecule. When this DNA reproduces itself inside the bacterial cell, it usually reproduces itself with high fidelity. It makes an exact and faithful copy of itself, which we'll illustrate with a short fragment of the molecule.

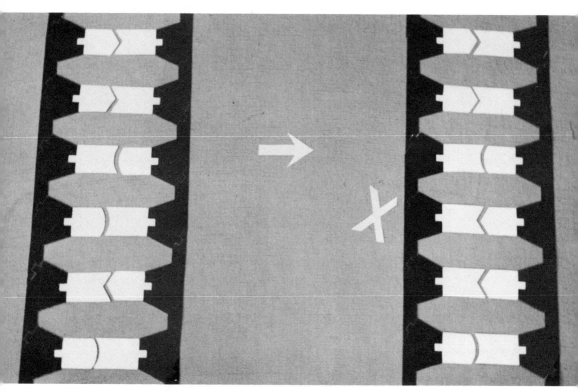

But once in every 10,000 or so times something goes wrong in this copying process. Working down along the DNA fiber, unit by unit, a faithful copy is being made. But at some point an error occurs; the message in the original DNA has not been copied correctly. From this point on, however, the rest of the DNA fiber is reproduced perfectly.

The new DNA molecule is like the parental DNA in every respect except for one point at which an error has been made. And when it reproduces itself, it will of course reproduce the error.

Any virus particle which manages to draw one of these mutant DNA molecules as its genetic material will then be a mutant virus; it will pass on this mutant property to all of its descendants.

Mutation, or copy error, is not the only way in which new varieties of viruses can occur. There is a second way, and that is the process of *genetic recombination*. For even organisms as small as these bacterial viruses have something which resembles a sexual process.

In the experiments we have considered until now, the bacterial cell was always infected by a single virus, and the offspring viruses were always the descendants of just that single parent virus. But it is also possible that two different kinds of virus particles can simultaneously infect the same bacterial cell. And in that case, it is found that among the offspring of these two virus particles there will be a certain number which have derived some of their hereditary properties from one parent and some of their properties from the other parent.

Before we can consider the experiments which demonstrate such sexual processes among the viruses, we must consider another type of mutant.

If we look again at thousands of plaques we will find another variant plaque, the small, turbid plaque, which is quite different from the clear plaques we have been dealing with so far. If we isolate the virus col-

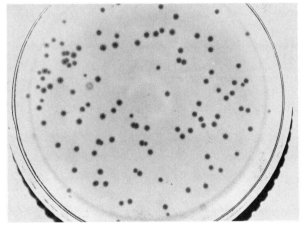

ony from such a plaque, all the bacteriophages in this variant plaque will now produce turbid instead of clear plaques. Thus we are now in possession of three hereditarily different virus types: the original small, clear-plaque forming type; the large, clear type which was the first mutant we isolated; and now a second mutant, the small, turbid-plaque forming type. For the sake of brevity, we will omit the phrase "plaque forming" in the following and refer to the virus types simply as "small and clear" etc., remembering that it is not the virus itself that is small and clear but rather the plaque which it forms.

Now let us infect a bacterium not with just a single virus, but let us infect it with one virus of the large, clear variety and one virus of the small, turbid variety. In other words, we are making what amounts to a cross, a genetic cross, of two virus types. We then incubate these virus-infected bacteria for the usual 30 minutes. At the end of 30 minutes, several hundred offspring viruses will emerge from the cell. We then put these offspring viruses on a jelly surface and see what kind of plaques they will make. We find the following results:

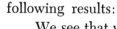

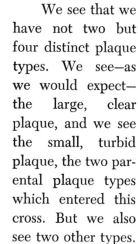

We see that we have not two but four distinct plaque types. We see—as we would expect— the large, clear plaque, and we see the small, turbid plaque, the two parental plaque types which entered this cross. But we also see two other types. We see, first of all, the small, clear plaque; but we also see a plaque which we have never seen before, namely a large, turbid plaque.

Now these two new types—the small and clear, and the large and turbid—which have appeared among the offspring of this cross, must represent genetic recombinants. The virus making the small, clear plaque must have derived its "clear" character from the "large, clear" parent, and it must have derived its "small" character from the "small, turbid" parent.

Similarly, the large turbid virus must have obtained its "large" character from the first parent and its "turbid" character from the second parent.

Now how do these genetic recombinants arise in the process of intracellular growth? They arise by a process which has been called "copy choice."

In order to understand the nature of the copy choice process, we can visualize the genetic structure—that is, the DNA of these viruses —in some symbolic form, say, as a straight line.

The first of the two parents—the large, clear parent—can be represented as having somewhere along its DNA fiber a marker of some kind, a characteristic which spells out the ability to cause large bacterial plaques. And somewhere else there must be another site at which the DNA carries the information which will ultimately cause the virus to make clear plaques.

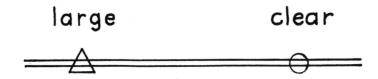

The second of the two parents—the small, turbid one—can be represented by a second straight line. This line will have markers determining plaque size and turbidity located at corresponding points along the line, that is, along the DNA molecule of the virus.

At one point is a marker which determines that the virus will make small plaques; at the other point is a marker which determines that the virus will make turbid plaques.

We have, then, two parental virus types which find themselves within the same bacterial cell at the outset of the infection.

Now, let us imagine that one of the two parental DNA molecules serves as a template for the production of DNA fibers to be incorporated into one of its descendants. As the new molecule builds up, unit by unit, it copies this parent DNA molecule, incorporating the "large" characteristic into its own structure.

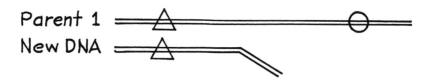

But if, somewhere within that mixedly infected cell, the second type of parental DNA is in the neighborhood, then the possibility exists that the copy process will not continue using the DNA molecule of the first parent as its template. Instead, a switch, or "copy choice," may take place so that the copy process is continued and completed using the DNA of the second parent. This segment of the new DNA molecule will then include the turbid marker copied from the second parent.

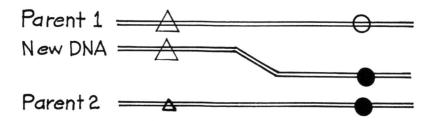

Therefore, the DNA molecule constructed by this copy choice process will carry the large marker at one end and the turbid marker at the other. The resulting virus will be of a new type; it will be of the large, turbid variety.

We have seen now two very different ways in which new kinds of viruses may occur in nature. We saw, first of all, that copy errors can occur during the course of self-duplication and that these will give rise to new virus types, to virus mutants. Secondly, we saw that viruses are capable of "crossbreeding"; when two bacterial viruses with different hereditary characteristics infect the same bacterial cell, we are likely to get virus recombinants, new viruses which have derived some of their genetic properties from one type of virus and some of their properties from a different virus type.

The study of mutation in bacterial viruses is important for a number of reasons.

It has helped us in appreciating the role of mutation in viral diseases. In viruses which infect man, for example, we now understand that immunity developed today against an established virus might not be of any help against a mutant of that virus which may occur tomorrow. Perhaps if we learn enough about virus mutation, it might someday be possible to control this process in some degree.

Bacterial viruses also have proven themselves to be an excellent laboratory tool for the study of genetics, the science of heredity. No other organisms can produce a new generation of several hundred progeny every half hour and billions of progeny in half a day. No other organism can be manipulated so easily and handled so cheaply.

DNA, the germinal substance of bacterial viruses, is also the essential hereditary material of all living organisms and thus controls the activity of living cells of every kind. Yet it is only in the virus that we can study its reproduction and function so readily. That is because the nucleic acid in living cells is hopelessly lost among the thousands of other materials of which a cell is made.

In a more general way, the study of mutation among viruses is also an experiment in evolution, and it shows very clearly that the chief mechanism of evolution is error and imperfection, that is, the inability of living organisms to always make perfect copies of themselves.

The students of bacterial viruses have already answered some of the classical problems of biology. Furthermore, they have raised a whole crop of new problems. Finally, they are giving us new clues in our efforts to control viral diseases and fresh perspectives on such important questions as the nature, identity and function of the genetic material, which is the most fundamental substance of all living things.

GUNTHER S. STENT

When a Virus Isn't a Virus

A VIRUS "comes to life" the moment it infects a cell.

The period immediately following is the time—and the only time —during which the virus exhibits essential properties of a "living organism." It reproduces, and it may mutate.

We might ask a seemingly straightforward question at this point: where *is* the virus, now that reproduction is underway?

In the case of the bacteriophage we can locate part of the virus, but this part is just the protein, the very part which seems to be superfluous insofar as reproduction is concerned. The DNA has disappeared.

We are tempted to say that the virus is now somewhere inside the cell, but we have clearly defined a virus as a nucleoprotein, and neither the protein alone nor the nucleic acid alone can rightly be called a virus.

We have to admit that the infecting bacteriophage no longer exists as a virus particle. The question, "where is the virus?" now becomes, "where are the pieces?"

The pieces we are looking for, of course, are essentially two in number. We can see both of them in the remarkable electron micrograph on the opposite page. The bacteriophage in the photograph has been deliberately exploded. The collapsed protein coat is below, and the tangled, broken threads of DNA which have been expelled from it lie sprawled across the upper half of the picture.

We have already learned that this viral DNA is injected into the bacterium at the moment of infection while the protein remains outside. But can we prove it? Can we really find the DNA inside the bacterial cell and the protein on the outside?

It would be most convenient if we could somehow label these

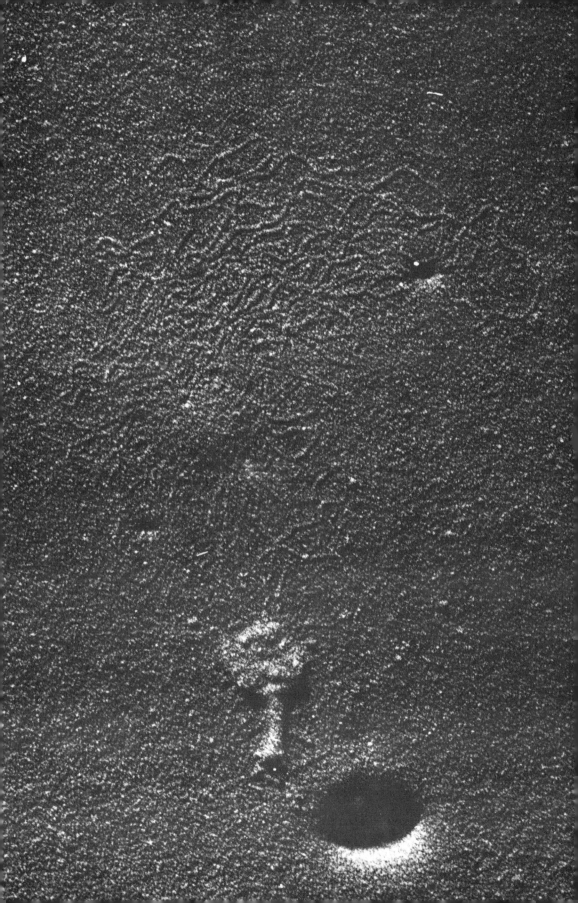

two parts of the virus independently and follow the fate of each as infection progresses.

Such labeling is quite possible today, thanks to the availability of radioactive tracer elements. Since DNA contains phosphorus and virus protein does not, we can "tag" the DNA by constructing a virus from raw materials containing radioactive phosphorus.

We simply add a little radiophosphorus to the food supply of a growing colony of bacteria. Bacteria cannot distinguish between radiophosphorus and the common form of the element which is part of their normal diet, so they ingest both varieties and quickly become radioactive.

When viruses are allowed to infect these radioactive bacteria and reproduce inside them, the resulting virus progeny also will be radioactive.

We can now isolate the viruses and detect their radioactivity with a Geiger counter. We know that this radioactivity indicates the presence of DNA, and we can thus keep track of the DNA wherever it may go. In a similar manner we can label the protein. We use radiosulfur in this case since viral protein contains sulfur but DNA does not.

All that remains to be done is to infect a fresh, nonradioactive colony of bacteria with labeled viruses and see what happens, first to the protein, then to the DNA.

We allow the infection to progress for a few minutes. Then we put the bacteria in a Waring blendor, which literally shaves them, stripping off whatever particles may be stuck to their outer membranes. These particles are separated from the bacteria by centrifuging, and both the particles and the bacteria are checked for radioactivity. We find in the case of protein-tagged viruses that the radioactivity resides in the stripped-off particles and not in the bacterial cells. This proves that the protein remained on the outside of the bacterial cells. It also proves that the protein is not needed to produce infection, for the experiment does not interfere with the reproduction of viruses within the freshly shaven bacterial cells. When we repeat the experiment, using viruses with tagged DNA, the radioactivity is found within the bacterial cells and not within the stripped-off protein. We know, then, that the DNA alone has entered the bacteria and that it alone must be responsible for the production of new viruses. This experiment with radioactive phosphorus and sulfur was first carried out by Alfred D. Hershey and Martha Chase in 1952.

Electron micrography confirms the fact that the protein is left outside. On the following page, we can see the empty phage coats clinging to an infected bacterium, and in the lower picture we can compare one of these empty jackets with a "healthy" phage particle which still contains its bundled-up strand of DNA.

To discover what the DNA inside an infected bacterium looks like is quite another problem. We know from radioactive tracer studies that it is there, but we have no direct evidence to indicate where it goes inside the cell, whether or not it remains in one piece, or just how it goes about directing the manufacture of new viruses.

Nor do we know how the DNA of the new viruses is put together.

We do know, however, where some of the raw materials for the new DNA come from. It was once thought that new viruses were made entirely from materials present in the bacterium at the time of infection. But in 1946 Seymour S. Cohen, at the University of Pennsylvania, proved this to be a false assumption.

Cohen infected bacteria with viruses and at the same time added radiophosphorus to the bacteria's food supply. When he isolated and tested the new generation of viruses resulting from the infection, he found them to be radioactive. In fact, they had about two-thirds as high a concentration of radiophosphorus as the food-laden medium on which the bacteria had been feeding since infection began. Thus, Cohen showed that most of the material from which the new viruses were made came from food ingested by the bacteria *after* they were infected. Further experiments by Gunther Stent and Ole Maaloe at the State Serum Institute of Denmark established that bacteria suddenly begin to take in more phosphorus at the time of infection and that most of this phosphorus goes directly into the assembling of new viruses. It takes the bacteria at least 12 minutes to convert the newly acquired phosphorus into viral DNA.

These findings lead to the conclusion that an infected cell provides a prodigious amount of "manual labor" for the sake of the virus which is destroying it. A virus needs more than a quietly alive cell

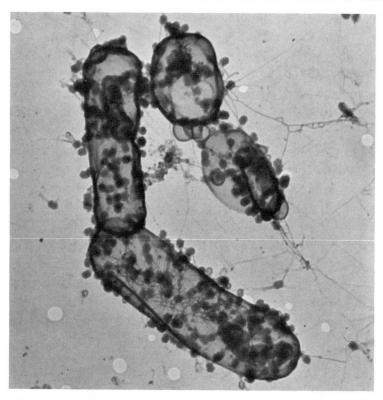

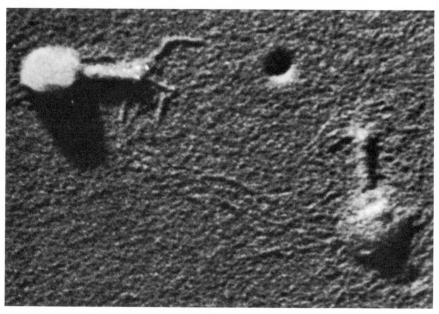

if it is going to multiply; it requires a cell functioning at top efficiency and it requires the presence of an adequate food supply from which the cell can draw raw materials.

It begins to appear that the virus itself is not "living" very energetically, even at the instant it is said to be most like a living organism. Not only does the virus "come apart" and lose its identity as a nucleoprotein, but it lets the cell do all the work.

This behavior may appear to be laziness, but at second glance it looks more like ingeniousness. It suggests that the virus may really be one of the most efficient machines in nature. The virus is an extremely simple structure compared to the cell, and yet it is able to make the very most of its environment and to mobilize the entire machinery of the cell for its own purposes. In addition, the structural simplicity of the virus particle permits it to exist in a state of suspended animation for years, dependent neither upon the cell nor upon any other source of energy. In its "lifelike" state, a virus is more fully dependent than any other living organism, while in its "lifeless" state as a molecule it is by all odds the least dependent. If self-sufficiency were the criterion of "life," the virus would only qualify when it is most certainly "dead."

We seem to have returned to the old, insoluble question, "is the virus a living thing or just a molecule?" Perhaps we are now in a position to suggest a way out of this dilemma, at least for the moment. Let's consider not the whole virus but only the DNA of the virus. What is the most striking feature of viral DNA? Whenever we find viral DNA without its protein, it is deep within a cell, and we can see that it is not behaving very much like an organism *or* like a single molecule. Rather, it is acting as if it were an integral part of the cell itself.

The viral DNA interacts intimately with many specialized components of the cell; and the cell, instead of resisting this "infective" fragment of a virus, eagerly accepts it. The viral DNA, in short, behaves more like a familiar piece of the cellular machinery gone wrong than like a foreign invader. This concept does not deny the validity of labeling the virus either "molecule" or "organism"; but it does enable us to better appreciate the insidious power of the virus— whatever its label—to cause disease.

"VIRUS" AS A DISEASE

AGENT PROVOCATEUR

THIS ANCIENT hieroglyph shows an Egyptian with a withered leg, probably the result of poliomyelitis.

Polio, smallpox and many other virus infections were familiar to man long before anyone knew what caused disease. Not until the 1870's was it proved—by Louis Pasteur and Robert Koch—that many infectious diseases were caused by "germs," that is, by bacteria. It was another 30 years before viruses, too, were established as a cause of disease.

The most obvious difference between bacteria and viruses is that bacteria can be seen with a light microscope while viruses, with one or two borderline exceptions, cannot. The volume of the average germ is perhaps 10,000 times as great as that of the average virus.

A more significant difference between the two is that a bacterium is relatively independent and can grow and reproduce almost anywhere, whereas a virus can multiply and cause disease only within a living cell. This difference implies a further distinction between bacterium and virus which is of primary importance to our understanding of the mechanics of virus infection.

The bacterium is an aggressive animal that literally attacks the cells or tissues of its victims. The two, the bacterium and the cells it attacks, often engage in mortal combat which results in the victory of one or the other.

The virus, on the other hand, could neither reproduce nor cause disease without the wholehearted co-operation of the invaded cell. Although a cell is often able to resist the initial attachment of a virus to its outer wall, it becomes complacent once the nucleic acid of the virus has gotten inside; in fact, the cell then goes out of its way to provide everything the virus asks for, seemingly unaware of the fact that it is thereby sealing its own doom.

The only way a virus can succeed in killing or injuring the relatively gigantic cell is by forgoing the technique of frontal attack in favor of seduction and subversion. In short, the virus—or, more correctly, the nucleic acid of the virus—operates as if it were a fully functioning constituent of the cell it invades. The normal components of the cell, on their part, accept the viral nucleic acid and co-operate with it even more energetically than they do with the nucleic acid of the cell itself.

The virus thus fulfills rather well the role of *agent provocateur*, "one employed to associate himself with members of a group and by pretended sympathy with their aims lead them to commit overt illegal or harmful acts, especially so they may be apprehended and punished."

In some cases, a virus may go in for long-range espionage and "lie low" within the cell for generations, making one and only one replica of itself each time the cell divides. Such a *latent* virus may suddenly become active and kill; but for as long as it remains latent there is no way of distinguishing it from other parts of the cell. It does not just behave "as if" it were part of the cell; it *is* part of the cell.

There is only a limited number of cell types with which a particular virus is "compatible." Polio, for example, will not naturally infect frogs or tobacco plants. This fact leads some virologists to believe that the virus originally must have evolved from a cell component, from a functioning part of a cell which somehow "escaped" but was able periodically to "return home" and exist comfortably as an intracellular parasite.

Whatever may have been the origin of viruses, the most distinctive characteristic shared by all of them is their talent for intimate cohabitation with cellular components inside the cell. This same property clearly distinguishes viral infection from bacterial infection and makes virus diseases highly resistant to treatment; as long as a virus acts like an integral part of a cell, it is difficult, if not impossible, to destroy the virus without also destroying the cell.

Ironically, the virus gains nothing whatever from destroying a cell or causing disease. From the virus's point of view, the death of a cell is an incidental and often unfortunate by-product of virus reproduction. The death of a man or animal or plant is, in turn, the result of the collective death of a large number of cells. Neither dead cells nor dead organisms are of any use to a virus.

Disease is also a disadvantage to the virus because it leads to both natural and synthetic antivirus defenses on the part of living organisms. Plants and animals often develop resistance to viruses, and they are more likely to thrive than are their susceptible cousins. Man makes it still more difficult for the virus when he responds to disease by inventing such antivirus weapons as vaccines.

But neither vaccines nor natural immunity can help a cell once the nucleic acid of a virus has gotten inside. From this point on, the cell is inevitably a helpless and willing victim.

In the following two chapters, Arthur Pardee and Harry Rubin explain how viruses manage to redirect the functions of infected cells and how this process results in the specific diseases with which we are unhappily familiar. Dr. Pardee will discuss the chemical ingenuity which makes the virus such a successful *agent provocateur* inside the living cell. Dr. Rubin will discuss the differences between viruses which kill cells and viruses which cause cells to reproduce wildly in the form of tumors.

How DO viruses manage to harm us? How do they make us sick, paralyze us, cause cancers, or kill us? If we knew more about how viruses manage to do these things, we would perhaps be able to prevent some of their distressing activities.

The first thing that strikes us about a virus is that it is very small, and yet it is able to do a great deal of damage which we can observe all too easily.

If we think about the way a virus acts, we realize that it doesn't attack us all at once; it attacks us cell by cell. So we will

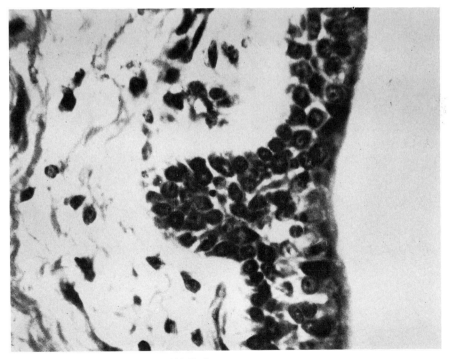

be very much concerned with the cell, the fundamental unit of which we are all made.

The human cells on the previous page, which come from lung tissue, are just a few of the billions of cells in our bodies. Each of the little black objects is a cell, and each is capable of independent life.

What the viruses do is to attack these individual living cells and kill them. Viruses are much smaller than these cells, but they can damage them or destroy them, and when enough of the cells are killed, the animal itself dies.

In the case of polio, the viruses may attack only a few cells in the brain stem, but this is quite enough to kill.

How to approach this problem is another question. Many animals, and man in particular, are so complicated that we cannot readily study them. But we can choose creatures that are themselves single cells, and we can then investigate what happens when they are attacked by viruses.

In other words, we choose to work with a simpler model. We scientists often do this kind of thing, and it's a little embarrassing. It is rather like the story of the fellow who lost his keys in the dark and then looked for them under the lamp post because there was

more light there. We, too, always try to look where there is more light.

So we use bacteria for our experiments, several of which Dr. Stent has already described.

One of the basic experiments is quite simple. We take a flask and put in it a solution containing a little food and a large number of bacteria. The living bacteria cause the liquid to appear cloudy.

Now we add a large number of viruses—T2 bacteriophages—and put the flask in a warm bath. Such a bath normally encourages bacteria to grow and reproduce.

If we look at the flask again 25 minutes later, we find a striking change. The liquid has become clearer.

The reason is that the bacteria, which made the solution cloudy when they were alive, have been attacked, killed and broken up by the viruses.

How does this come about?

We have already seen how it comes about, for this clearing of the liquid is the visible effect of the completion of the viruses' life cycle, described on page 76.

The only difference is that what we see is the result of not one but billions of viruses simultaneously killing billions of bacteria.

Our question, however, is still basically unanswered. We do know that the genetic material of the virus enters the bacterium and, somehow, manages to duplicate itself several hundred times and dictate the manufacture of viral protein coats for new viruses. But the "somehow" remains to be explained.

Our problem here is to look more closely at what went on after the virus infected the bacterium. To do this, we can't use microscopes because microscopes can't see enough. We have to use chemical methods, methods concerned with chemical changes inside the bacterial cells.

Now, to talk about the chemistry of cells, we have to know something about the kinds of chemicals that occur in them. There is an enormous variety of chemicals involved.

Some of the most essential materials to be found in any normal cell include food, structural proteins, enzymes, and the cell's genetic material, nucleic acid.

Food is drawn in through a cell's walls from outside. It usually comes from some nutrient fluid such as blood, in the case of the higher animals, or a meat broth, or perhaps a solution of sugar and special salts, in the case of bacteria grown in a laboratory.

Structural proteins of many different kinds make up the body of the cell.

Enzymes, which are a particular form of protein, carry out many of the specialized reactions involved in the growth of a cell. They themselves are not permanently changed in the process. Enzymes are found in all living creatures, and they carry out thousands of reactions. They might be called the specialized workmen on the production lines of living cells. Each kind of enzyme carries out a specific function, usually something as simple as breaking apart a particular kind of molecule at a particular point or binding two molecules together in a particular way. Many common products, meat tenderizers and junket mixes, for example, work by virtue of the enzymes they contain.

Enzymes are very small, much smaller than viruses, and they are found in great numbers. Perhaps a million enzymes can be found in a single bacterial cell.

The genetic material of the cell, nucleic acid, is found in the cell's chromosomes. It is a very complicated chemical, constructed of thousands of small pieces strung together like links in a chain. Nucleic acid is a kind of chemical blueprint, for it determines the structure and function of the cell; for example, it may make the cell develop into a bacterium, or an elephant cell, or a corn husk cell.

In a normal bacterial cell, incoming particles of food are broken down and are used partly for energy. Under the control of the cell's genetic material, aided by existing bacterial enzymes, the food products are changed into different proteins, enzymes and nucleic acid characteristic of the bacterium.

This process goes on at an incredible speed; billions of changes of this sort occur every hour in every tiny bacterial cell. A duplicate copy of the bacterium's nucleic acid is completed in the course of an hour or less. Then the entire cell proceeds to divide, forming two bacteria in place of the original "parent" bacterium.

We can see that these bacteria are quite busy taking in food, growing, and making new parts for themselves.

Now, what happens to these bacteria when viruses attack them?

The bacterial virus is a very different sort of organism from the bacterium. As we've already learned, it consists, essentially, of nothing more than a coat of protein wrapped around a strand of nucleic acid. It is far from self-sufficient, for it has no independent source of energy and is quite unable to process any kind of food. It solves this problem by imprinting its own growth pattern on the bacterial cell. In effect, it substitutes its own blueprint, its own genetic material, for that of the bacterium. This causes the bacterium to forget its own needs and concentrate on producing new viruses instead of new bacteria. We can imagine the bacterial cell as a sort of factory normally engaged in manufacturing parts for new factories of the same kind. The virus, then, would be like an invading army which converts the factory from the manufacture of factory machinery to the manufacture of bullets.

Two different processes are involved: halting the normal chemistry of the bacterium and starting up the chemistry of virus multiplication.

When the virus has attached itself to the bacterium and injected its nucleic acid, the destructive process begins with the production of enzymes which fasten themselves to the nucleic acid of the bacterium and crumble it into pieces by breaking it up chemically. Once this genetic material of the bacterium is destroyed, no new bacterial parts can be created. The machinery of the cell continues to function, however, taking in food and producing energy and protein for the sole benefit of the virus.

Next, the viral nucleic acid directs the production of other kinds of enzymes. Some of these new, subversive enzymes actually rob the old bacterial enzymes of their food so that they can no longer function. Others begin to assemble chemical units to form the material of new viruses.

About six minutes after infection, the bacterial cell begins to produce new fibers of viral nucleic acid. Soon after this, the cell also produces subunits of viral protein. The manufacture of viral nucleic acid and protein continues for about 12 minutes, and many duplicates of each are formed.

The protein subunits begin to collect around each of the new viral nucleic acid fibers during the final 10 minutes. These immature viruses can be seen within the bacterial cell on the following page. The electron micrograph, prepared by Dr. Edward Kellenberger and his colleagues at the University of Geneva, shows an unshadowed, ultrathin section of several infected bacteria. The dark spots are dense condensations of DNA surrounded by membranes of protein. These membranes are difficult to detect because the immature bacteriophage particles are seen in cross section. Whether or not protein "tails" are attached is not known; the tails, if present, would

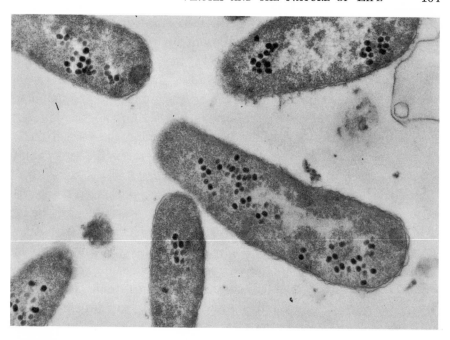

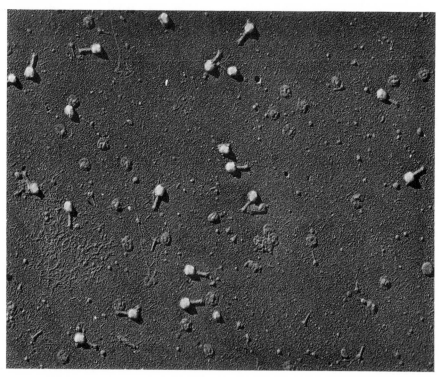

not be dense enough to register in the electron microscope.

If the bacteria are broken open at this stage, we find the particles shown in the lower electron micrograph: complete new phage particles; empty protein "heads"; a few unattached protein "tails"; and, at the lower left, what is apparently broken fragments of DNA. The empty protein "heads" represent the "heads" of immature phages which were too fragile to withstand the shock that resulted from breaking open the bacterial cells. The DNA was probably "exploded" out of one of these heads by the same shock.

Near the end of the reproductive cycle, the bacterium is crowded with some 200 to 300 newly made viruses. At this time, still another kind of enzyme is produced. These enzyme molecules break open the outer "skin" of the bacterium, allowing the new viruses to escape.

After the viruses have escaped from the bacterium, they go their own way. They are free to infect and destroy thousands of other bacterial cells. In fact, the viruses eventually can destroy all the bacteria in the culture, which was the case when our bacterial solution cleared half an hour after viruses had been added to the flask. All the cells were killed, and those which still could be seen under a microscope were mere ghosts of their former, robust selves. Originally, the bacteria looked like fat sausages full of enzymes, proteins and other components. After infection, as we can see in this

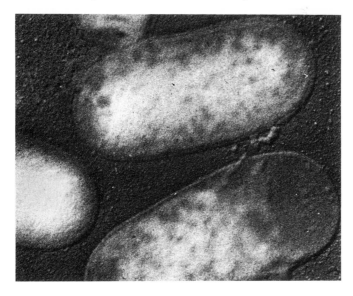

electron micrograph, they are simply empty bags containing very little of their original material, too flattened out even to cast a shadow. They have been dissolved, or *lysed,* by viruses, and they are unable to carry on any sort of chemical activity.

So far, we have been studying only one particular kind of virus, a bacterial virus with the name T2. But the behavior of T2 inside the bacterium serves as a model to help us understand how other viruses act.

Other viruses differ from bacterial viruses in size, shape, and chemical make-up. As we know, the genetic material of bacterial viruses and a number of others is deoxyribonucleic acid, or DNA, while the genetic material of others, like polio, is the closely related compound, ribonucleic acid, or RNA.

Each kind of virus also has its own distinctive protein.

Another difference is that various kinds of viruses may have quite different effects on cells. The action of the polio virus is comparable with that of the bacterial viruses; the polio virus lyses the cell, and newly formed viruses escape. On the other hand, with diseases like influenza and mumps, the new viruses leak slowly out of the infected cell, and the cell is not decomposed by the virus.

Another group of viruses causes cancers by stimulating abnormal growth in the infected cells rather than killing them. Still other viruses—for example, the pox virus—kill cells in a local area and cause the appearance of pustules which, if the victim lives, eventually heal but leave deep scars.

Smallpox, polio, and a few other virus infections can be stopped by vaccination. But what about all the others? Can we ever learn to control them, and does the sort of information we've been discussing offer us any practical clues?

It seems possible that we might successfully use the techniques of chemotherapy and develop wonder drugs that would perhaps stop virus reactions. A number of very specific reactions occurring inside an infected cell are necessary if a virus is to multiply within the cell. If we can find a way of stopping these reactions in infected cells without stopping similar reactions in cells that are still healthy, then we may be able to stop a dangerous virus infection without killing the whole animal.

There are two problems involved in this approach, and these problems have not been solved satisfactorily. The first is the problem of stopping some cellular reactions without stopping similar reactions which are essential to healthy cells, and there seems to be a fair chance that we can learn how to do this.

The second problem is that of catching the virus infection before it is too late. If relatively few cells are killed, the animal will survive. But if too many cells are killed before the virus attack can be stopped, it does little good to keep the viruses from attacking further. The problem becomes one of diagnosing a virus infection before it can do irreparable damage.

There is also the possibility of finding chemicals which can be administered when a virus infection is first threatened, for example, in the case of an impending epidemic. Perhaps we could stop a virus infection by the use of drugs even before the infection gets started.

These are all problems for the future, and I'd like to point out that there is need for a very great deal of work in this field.

In any event, we hope that, as we learn more and more about the chemical processes that go on in infected cells, and as we learn more and more about the chemistry of viruses, we will be able to take some giant steps toward the goal of preventing virus diseases.

Arthur B. Pardee

KILLERS AND CARCINOGENS

IF WE THINK of virology in a narrow sense as the study of the physical and chemical nature of viruses, then its origin is rather easy to date. The most commonly accepted date is 1892 when Dmitri Iwanowski discovered a disease agent smaller than a bacterium.

Iwanowski extracted material from tobacco plants infected with the tobacco mosaic disease and passed this material through an ultra-fine filter which held back even the smallest bacteria. As we know, he found that there was something small enough to pass through this filter, yet capable of causing the same mosaic disease when inoculated into a healthy tobacco plant.

However, if we are more liberal and include as part of our definition of virology the study of virus diseases, then its history is far more venerable, dating way back before the Christian era.

Perhaps the most studied and best documented of all the virus diseases in history is the scourge of smallpox. This might be expected because smallpox was so widespread and so severe. It was known before the birth of Christ, particularly in Asia. It was brought to Europe in the 16th century, where it caused a number of serious epidemics.

Throughout the history of smallpox, people have been quite superstitious about its nature. But, remarkably enough, they made some astute observations. They realized that it was a single disease with a specific cause; they realized that it was contagious, that it spread from one human to another; and they even had a pretty good idea of how it spread. They were aware of the fact that the scabs which are the lesions of smallpox contained some kind of material which, when inoculated into a healthy man, would cause the same kind of disease.

Furthermore, they realized that when a person recovered from smallpox he became immune and could not be infected again when new epidemics of the disease appeared. Some unsung Ancient, probably in Asia, put two and two together and realized that, if he took the material from smallpox scabs and deliberately inoculated a healthy human being under the proper conditions, the inoculated individual frequently would develop a relatively mild case of smallpox and would then be immune when severe outbreaks of the disease occurred.

The only unfortunate aspect of this practice, which became very common in China and Turkey, and later in England, was the fact that "frequently" is not "always," and a large number of people died because inoculation could not be very well controlled.

However, the practice of inoculation, or variolation, as it was then called, was the logical predecessor of a discovery which, if measured in terms of value to human survival, is the most monumental in the history of virus diseases. This was the discovery of the present-day technique of vaccination against smallpox.

In the rural areas of England in the late 1700's, it was believed that anyone afflicted with cowpox would thereafter be immune to smallpox. Cowpox is a disease somewhat like smallpox but much milder. It can be contracted from cattle, as it often was by English milkmaids.

In general, this belief was scoffed at by the men of science. But there was one, Dr. Edward Jenner, who did not scoff. He believed it was true and, more importantly, he did some experiments. He removed scabs from cattle suffering from cowpox and inoculated material from the scabs directly into humans, including his own son. He found that human beings would then contract a mild case of cowpox and become immune to the more serious disease, smallpox.

Jenner's process was called vaccination, a name derived from *vacca,* the Latin word for cow.

Vaccination was commonly adopted throughout England, but it met with mixed public reaction. A cartoon of the time reflects a conviction on the part of many people that inoculation with cowpox would bestow on them a partly bovine nature.

These developments in the art of vaccination occurred some 100 years before the discovery of the true nature of viruses. Of course

The Bettmann Archive

we have learned a great deal about viruses since then, but there has been very little in the way of an improvement on Jenner's vaccine.

We should remember, however, that Jenner could not even have considered such things as vaccination without the accumulated knowledge of many centuries—basic information about the nature of smallpox, the spread of the disease, and immunity.

Today, the investigation of virus diseases is focused upon the interrelationships between viruses and the individual body cells which they infect.

The basic research tools used in this highly complex study are surprisingly simple, and are illustrated by the pipette, the fertile egg and the Petri dish.

The most important of the three is the pipette, used to obtain precise measurements of quantity; without precise techniques for measuring fluid volumes, we cannot carry out accurate scientific work.

The egg, our source of chicken embryos, has a long and honorable history in the study of animal viruses. It assumed a particularly important role in the period when it was necessary to study the multi-

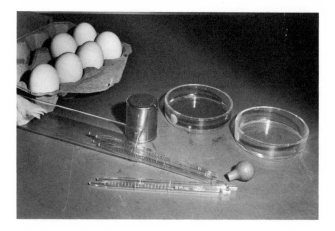

plication of viruses in whole, living organisms. Of all the animals that could be used, the chicken embryo was the most convenient.

The Petri dish is just a simple laboratory vessel, but it symbolizes one of the important new developments in animal virology. Beginning about 1950, techniques were discovered for removing embryos from the fertile egg, dispersing the cells, and then growing these living cells in a tissue culture where they could continue to reproduce themselves.

We simply crack open an egg, break through the membranes, and place the living embryo in a Petri dish.

Then we remove parts of the embryo and put them in a mixer. The purpose of the mixer is to agitate the cells of the embryo so they will become suspended in a liquid which we can handle easily.

When we put this suspension of chicken embryo cells in a Petri dish, the cells will settle on the glass, stick there, and multiply.

Now suppose we have a liquid solution containing a relatively light concentration of viruses and we wish to find out how many viruses are in the solution. We take up some of the solution in a pipette, measure it carefully, and add it to the cells in the Petri dish. As we've already seen in the case of bacterial viruses, every virus will infect a cell and multiply within it, killing the cell in the process. The new virus particles will be released from the cell and infect surrounding cells, where the process will be repeated. Within a period of several days, each virus colony has amassed a heap of dead cells. By counting these areas of dead cells, we can determine how many viruses we had added to the tissue culture; and from this figure we can determine the concentration of viruses in our original virus preparation.

The development of tissue culture techniques is important for a number of reasons. The first and most obvious is that it now becomes possible to study the multiplication of viruses under conditions in which we can continually observe the infected cell from the moment the virus gets into the cell until the moment it destroys the cell.

Secondly, we also can make very precise measurements of the number of viruses present in a particular suspension of viruses at any given time.

Finally, it has been possible to grow isolated human cells in tissue culture and to study the effects of viruses such as poliomyelitis on the cells of human beings. Before the advent of tissue culture, virus research in diseases affecting man was seriously restricted; obviously, you cannot infect a man with polio just to see what will happen.

A particularly popular tool in the tissue culture of human cells is the HeLa cell, which supports very beautifully the growth of poliomyelitis virus. HeLa cells are the descendants of cancerous cells taken from a patient named He....La...., and grown successfully in tissue culture. Another very useful human cell is that of the amnion, which is part of the membrane surrounding the baby at birth. The HeLa cell and the human amnion cell have taught us a great deal about the behavior of polio viruses in man.

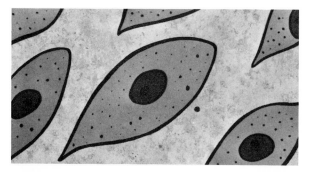

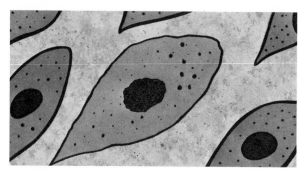

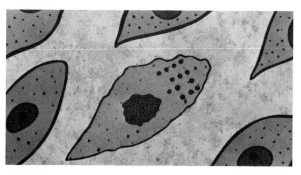

These drawings illustrate what happens to human cells in tissue culture when poliomyelitis virus is allowed to attack them.

The black dot represents a polio virus about to enter a cell. For several hours after the virus penetrates the cell, we see no changes whatever, although there are profound submicroscopic changes occurring in the structure of the virus particle.

The first thing we do see is a change in the center of the cell, in the nucleus. The multiplying virus particles are first seen within the cytoplasm of the cell, which undergoes degenerative changes. New viruses are gradually released, and finally the cell disintegrates, scattering the remaining virus particles.

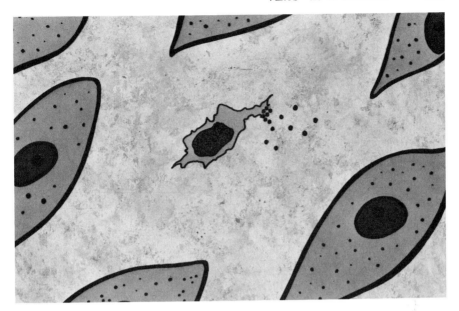

This process of the penetration of the virus, the multiplication of the virus and its release, followed by the death of the cell is repeated over and over. Each cell releases hundreds, even thousands of virus particles to infect the surrounding cells. After the cycle has been repeated many times, we have a sizable area of dead cells in the tissue culture. This area of dead cells, surrounded by living cells, is called a plaque and is plainly visible. By simply counting the number of plaques, we can determine the number of virus particles initially present.

By studying the changes in the cells and the time it takes for a virus to multiply and break open the cell, we can get a good idea of how a single virus particle manages to get into a cell, multiply in it, destroy it, and subsequently cause the death of a whole group of cells in the neighborhood.

We have seen here what a virus does to an individual cell or a group of similar cells. But what does this mean in terms of disease which a physician can diagnose? Can we project this sequence of cellular events onto the human organism as a whole? We can do this, albeit in a rough way, although the picture becomes much more complicated.

When polio viruses infect a human being, they multiply in tissues of various types and finally cause the typical symptoms of poliomyelitis.

The viruses enter through the gastro-intestinal tract, resulting

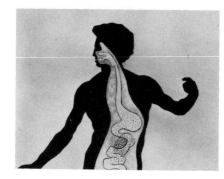

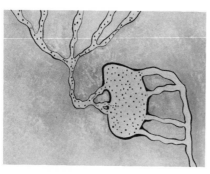

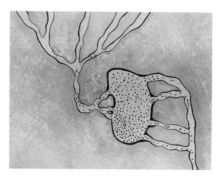

in infection of cells which line the walls of the intestine. Here the virus multiplies and proceeds to spread through the lymphatic system into the lymph nodes.

Very frequently, the infection stops here, but occasionally the viruses continue to multiply and make their way past the lymph nodes, which normally serve as filters of foreign, unwanted substances in the body. When this happens, the virus particles get into the blood stream and are carried to other parts of the body, most critically to the central nervous system. The multiplication of polio viruses in the spinal cord and the brain stem produces the disease we call poliomyelitis.

When the viruses multiply in the individual cells of the central nervous system, they reproduce the sequence of events which we previously followed in the case of individual cells in an infected tissue culture. However, this time we are dealing with the essential cells of the nervous system, those cells which control the movement of muscles or, in the case of the brain stem, those which

control such important functions as breathing. If the virus
multiplies in enough of these
cells and destroys their function, the result is paralysis—of
a limb, perhaps, or of those
muscles which control breathing. This is why such devices
as the iron lung are used in
poliomyelitis therapy.

Poliomyelitis, of course,
is only one of many diseases
caused by viruses. Like polio,
most are caused by cytocidal
(cell-killing) viruses. These
include yellow fever, equine
encephalitis, rabies and smallpox. There is another class of
viruses that is not so well
known to most people but that
may prove to be considerably
more important than the cell-
killing viruses. This second
class is that of the tumor viruses. These viruses multiply
inside cells much more slowly
than do the cell-killing variety; instead of killing the cell,
they cause the cell itself to
multiply under conditions
where it normally would not
multiply.

The first of the tumor viruses to be clearly established
as such was the Rous sarcoma
virus, discovered by Dr. Peyton Rous in 1911 at the Rocke-

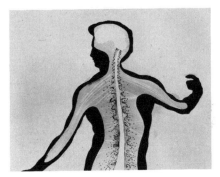

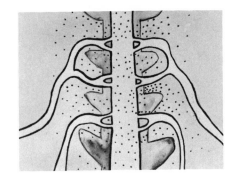

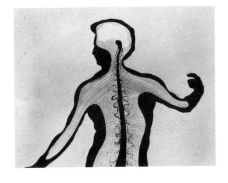

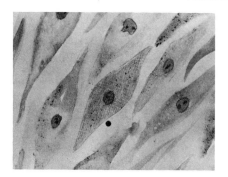

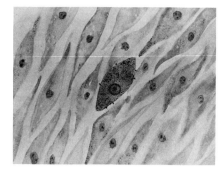

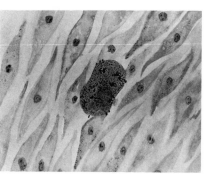

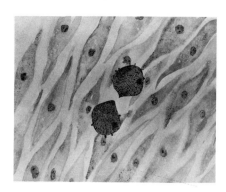

feller Institute in New York. It was recovered from a cancer, called a sarcoma, growing in the breast muscle of a Plymouth Rock hen. Dr. Rous first found that he could reproduce the tumor in another chicken by injecting cells from the original tumor. He then made an extract from the tumors, passed it through a filter which held back living cells, and was able to cause cancer by injecting the cell-free material into another chicken. Since that time, a great variety of viruses has been found to be associated with cancer, but the Rous sarcoma virus probably has been studied more thoroughly than any of the others.

Recently, techniques have been developed for infecting normal chicken cells in tissue culture with Rous sarcoma virus, and transforming them into cancer cells.

We start with a group of normal cells from a chicken embryo, which are growing in a Petri dish. The cells lie in a flat mat across the surface of the tissue culture.

A Rous sarcoma virus particle, represented by a black dot, comes in contact with a susceptible cell and disappears into the cell.

It begins to multiply within the cell, and soon we begin to see some changes occurring in the cell. The cell becomes rather granular and begins to swell up.

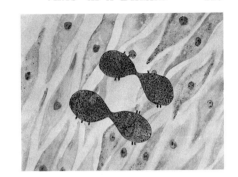

The infected cell now begins to divide, even though the other, normal cells remain relatively inactive. These normal cells had already multiplied until they crowded the surface of the dish in a single layer; they then stopped growing and multiplying.

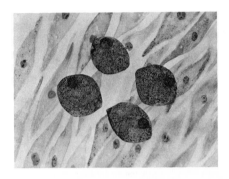

But the crowded conditions don't seem to bother the cells infected with the Rous sarcoma virus. They continue to multiply, exhibiting one of the more important characteristics of cancer cells—the failure to recognize the limitations on growth and movement imposed on normal cells. The cancer cells continue to multiply and continue to produce and release viruses while remaining intact. The distorted cells, having no room within the orderly layer of normal cells, pile up on top of one another, causing a microtumor —a small tumor that grows on top of the layer of normal

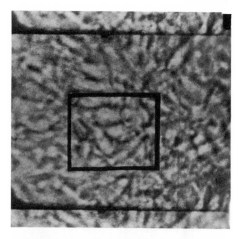

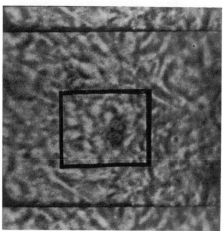

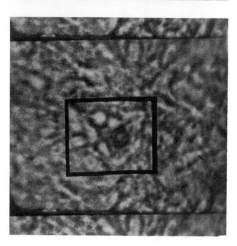

cells in the tissue culture.

These drawings actually represent no more than an idealized version of what we think happens when a tumor virus gets into a cell. To take serial photographs of what is actually going on is far more difficult.

But here are three frames from the first motion picture film we have ever taken—this was in 1960—of what happens to normal chicken cells when they are infected with Rous sarcoma viruses. The pictures are very crude, but if nothing else, their crudity serves to illustrate the fact that our techniques are far from perfect even in this day of technical refinement.

Several of the cells inside the rectangle have been infected with the virus. All the other cells are normal and healthy.

The infected cells begin to round up, and they are very active when compared with the cells on the periphery.

There is some type of information that inhibits the normal cells from multiplying. The infected cells, however, begin to divide, and you can see the result of an abnormal

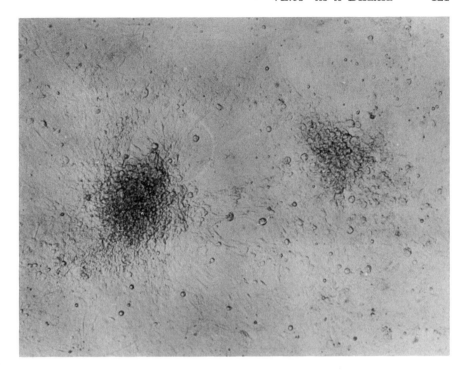

cell division. The resulting microtumor consists of hundreds of cells and is therefore not so difficult to photograph. Seen through the microscope, these two microtumors caused by the Rous sarcoma virus show clearly on top of a layer of healthy chicken cells.

What we have seen is the simplest possible sequence of events following the infection of a cell by a tumor virus. We have been dealing with an isolated sheet of cells, and we have here none of the complications involved when the whole organism is affected.

What happens when we put the virus into a live chicken?

We believe that a series of events quite similar to the one we've seen in tissue culture occurs. We know that we can see a tumor—a cancer—within a few days after infection, and by the end of a week the tumor grows to considerable size. The tumor spreads throughout the animal and eventually causes its death.

We do not know whether all tumors are caused by viruses. However, we feel that we have an ideal model of tumor development in our demonstration of the effect of the Rous sarcoma virus on individual cells in tissue culture. This gives us a useful system for studying the onset of malignancy, and we believe it will have some application in understanding the onset of other malignancies as well.

We have talked about some of the most recent research in modern virology which has led to improved understanding of what happens when a cell is invaded by a viral parasite. As a result of these investigations, we have been able to make a number of important improvements and refinements in vaccines and in methods of preventing virus diseases.

When an epidemic occurs today, we can frequently isolate the responsible virus, identify it, and make a vaccine to counteract it.

In addition, the refinement of tissue culture techniques has made it possible to grow viruses which previously could not be grown, and this has led to such developments as the Salk polio vaccine.

However, there has been no fundamental improvement in our methods of dealing with viruses. Vaccination is still the only tool we have for preventing virus diseases since we have no really effective way of treating a virus disease once visible symptoms appear.

When we consider the reasons for this, it seems quite obvious that this should be so. After all, viruses are made of the same building blocks of which cells are made. Perhaps more important is the fact that the virus has no machinery of its own for making more virus. It can only reproduce within a living cell, and it does this by using the machinery by which the cell normally manufactures the material for its own growth and reproduction. The virus usurps this machinery to make more viruses, and as a result the cell is damaged in one way or another. The cell is either killed or it becomes a cancer cell.

It is evident that any chemical which will interfere with virus multiplication will probably also damage normal cells in the body. We have not yet found anything which can destroy a virus without also destroying the cells in which the virus multiplies.

We can take heart, however, from the obvious fact that the human organism during its evolution has developed defense mechanisms to deal quite effectively with virus diseases. Almost everyone has had, and has recovered from, a variety of virus diseases. It is realistic to expect that we shall learn a great deal more within the next few years about how the body deals with virus infection.

At present, we know only that the classical immunological reactions, such as the formation of circulating antibodies known in bacterial infections, do not play the only role in combating a primary virus infection and, indeed, may play a minor role. The nature of the other factors involved will become clearer within the next few years.

In the meantime, we as virologists obtain a great deal of satisfaction from the realization that we are learning something about a very complex but fascinating biological problem.

Harry Rubin

VERSATILE VENOM

As FAR AS we know, snakes are immune to all viruses. So, apparently, are yeasts, fungi, mollusks, and cone-bearing evergreens.

But practically all other species and orders of animals and plants, from germs to fish to man, are subject to virus disease. Birds and mammals are particularly susceptible, and man is perhaps the most vulnerable of all.

Some undiscovered virus is often blamed by physicians when the reason for an illness cannot be found; and in view of the pace at which new viruses are being discovered, the doctor is probably right. More than 200 previously unknown viruses causing disease in man have been discovered since 1955, and the number is still increasing.

Viruses are responsible for more illness than any other class of parasites; they cause blindness, deafness, paralysis, heart defects, mental deficiency, congenital defects and, at least in some plants and animals, cancer. Symptoms may be local, like the plaques appearing in a colony of infected bacteria, or like the lesions on a tobacco leaf or on the face of a smallpox victim. They may be general, like the withering of a plant or the wasting away of a human body. And any one of these symptoms can be caused by infection with a single virus particle.

Whereas such well-known diseases as tuberculosis, pneumonia, typhoid and leprosy are caused by bacteria, the list of familiar virus diseases includes measles, mumps, chicken pox, smallpox, influenza, poliomyelitis, yellow fever, and the common cold. Leukemia may well be caused by a virus, and some virologists suspect that viruses may be responsible for multiple sclerosis, Hodgkin's disease, mongolism, and even possibly schizophrenia.

The first animal virus to be identified was the tiny spherical particle responsible for hoof-and-mouth disease in cattle. It was discovered in 1898, less than a year after Beijerinck had named a virus as the cause of the mosaic disease in tobacco plants. The first virus to be identified with a disease in man was the yellow fever virus, discovered in 1901.

The relatively large influenza virus, shown here at a magnification of 110,000 diameters, affected 500,000,000 people throughout the world in 1918 and killed some 20,000,000; yet no one suspected a virus at the time, and it was not until 1931 that the murderous particle was identified.

Only in 1955 was the first "human virus" purified and crystallized so that it could be studied in detail; this virus was polio, crystallized at the University of California Virus Laboratory by Carlton E. Schwerdt and Frederick L. Schaffer.

The "human viruses" affect man in a variety of ways, psychological as well as physical.

The yellow fever virus has never been obtained in purified form, and no drug is known that will help the victim. It is so lethal that five scientists were killed by it while trying to describe it and find a cure.

Poliomyelitis paralyzes muscles by killing nerve cells in the gray matter of the spine. The name is a combination of the Greek words *polios*, meaning "gray," and *myelos*, meaning "marrow." The disease was at its worst in 1916 in New York City where it killed 2,000 people and paralyzed another 7,000.

Influenza was named by Italian astrologers who attributed epidemics to the "influence," or "emanation of occult power," from the stars. In the United States in 1918, the "influence" which the epidemic of "influenza germs" had on the public mind was reflected in newspaper headlines:

OCTOBER DRAFT CALL HALTED BY INFLUENZA
$1,000,000 TO COMBAT INFLUENZA
GAUZE MASKS MUST BE WORN ON STREETS
WOMAN WITH TWO HUSBANDS BLAMES "FLU"
ARE YOU WRITING THE BOYS IN QUARANTINE?

Measles, identified as a virus in 1911, is one of the earliest known virus diseases and was once regarded as a mild form of smallpox. The virus is responsible for several hundred thousand cases of measles and perhaps 300 deaths each year in the United States. The disease tends to occur in epidemics every two or three years. It is usually a disease of children.

German measles may cause all kinds of abnormalities in infants if mothers contract the disease during the first four months of pregnancy.

Chicken pox is a mild disease in children and adolescents, but in adults it causes the painful nerve inflammation known as shingles.

Hepatitis, a liver infection formerly called yellow jaundice, is extremely uncomfortable but seldom fatal. It was not identified as a virus disease until near the end of the Second World War. Two quite different strains of this virus are now recognized.

The herpes simplex, responsible for fever blisters and cold sores, is an "emotionally sensitive" virus which usually remains dormant but becomes active during periods of fatigue or emotional stress. It is present in most adults.

Other viruses, such as the Coxsackie viruses, the enteroviruses and the adenoviruses, represent whole groups of similar infectious particles.

The first Coxsackie virus was identified in 1947 as the cause of polio-like symptoms in two boys living in Coxsackie, N. Y. Some 30 other types are now known and all are found, like polio, in the human intestine.

About 25 different types of enteroviruses are also found, as their name implies, in the intestine. Originally, they were called ECHO viruses—Enteric Cytopathogenic Human Orphans, which means that they were found in the intestine, that they were cell-killers in man, and that each was a virus without a known disease to its name. They are now believed to cause the aches, pains and fevers associated with a number of grippe-like infections.

The 27 or more adenoviruses are all associated with respiratory infections, particularly in children. They cause sore throats, red eyes and aching joints in chimpanzees and monkeys as well as in man. They can be found in the adenoids at the back of the throat and can be grown in the laboratory in cultures of adenoid tissue.

The common cold is said to be caused by "a virus," but it should more properly be attributed to "viruses." A cold may be the result of infection by any of perhaps several dozen different kinds of virus or by a number of these viruses in concert. The adenoviruses are probably largely responsible, but the "common cold complex" is indeed complex. Colds with similar symptoms may well be caused by different viruses or by different combinations of viruses; and it is quite possible that one and the same virus may produce different symptoms in different people or under different conditions. The common cold represents one of the most tangled puzzles faced by virologists today.

Of course, not all virus diseases are necessarily "bad," and moral judgments often depend upon one's point of view. An extreme example of the relative "badness" of a virus is the case of the Spanish colonizers who considered smallpox "good" because it proved to be an effective weapon against native Mexican Indians.

Bacterial viruses are "good" insofar as they attack germs like cholera, although the viruses are not good enough to halt the progress of the disease. Bacterial viruses may even be helpful to the bacteria they infect, for in some cases they can carry genetic material from one kind of bacterium to another kind and thus enrich a particular bacterial strain.

Karl Maramorosch of the Rockefeller Institute recently showed that the aster-yellows virus can be most helpful to the corn leaf hopper which it infects, and he believes that many other "helpful" viruses eventually may be found in nature. The corn leaf hopper will die if it has no food other than healthy aster plants. It will thrive, however, on asters infected with the aster-yellows virus. Furthermore, the insect is able to survive on *healthy* asters once it has ingested viruses from infected plants. In some unknown way, the virus makes it possible for the leaf hopper to live on the healthy plants it previously had been unable to eat.

The very best viruses from man's point of view are those carefully cultivated strains of smallpox, polio and other viruses that are used in live-virus vaccines. These virus strains have been progressively weakened until they are able to confer immunity without themselves causing more than mild symptoms in man.

Live-virus vaccines lead to immunity in the same way that natural nonfatal infection leads to immunity.

When a man is infected by a disease for the first time, whether accidentally or through vaccination, his body reacts by producing antibodies which circulate in his blood. An antibody is a large molecule which will combine with a specific "foreign" substance and thus block the normal functioning of this substance, be it virus, germ or other poison. One type of antibody is useful only in combating the specific substance which caused the production of the antibody in the first place. If we are immune to ten different diseases, then we can be certain that we have at least ten different kinds of antibodies.

When a person is infected by a disease agent to which he is already immune by virtue of antibodies to this agent, the production of many more antibodies of the same kind is stimulated.

Most adults have had measles at one time or another and are therefore immune to the disease. But in certain South Sea Islands where the natives have never been exposed, a measles epidemic may be as serious as smallpox, killing old and young alike.

In the case of polio, most adults are immune because they have at some time contracted a mild case of the disease, often without ever being aware of it. Children raised in very sanitary surroundings are less likely than the average child to contract a mild, immunizing case of the disease; therefore, as adults they are more likely to be susceptible. Before the days of good sanitation and the polio vaccine, people usually either died of polio at a tender age or recovered and remained immune for life. Polio thus was seen most often among the very young and for this reason was called infantile paralysis.

The central problem in developing a vaccine against virus infection is that of finding a form of the virus which is able to stimulate the production of antibodies but still is not potent enough to cause more than a very mild disease reaction. There are two ways to solve this problem: kill the virus or attenuate it.

A virus that is inactivated, or "killed," will usually cause antibodies to be produced even though it is unable to infect living cells. However, it is not easy to "kill" a virus carefully enough to preserve its ability to stimulate immunity, and it is not always easy to be certain that every single virus in a large batch of vaccine is surely killed. One live virus in a billion billion may be quite enough to kill a man. One of the first really successful killed-virus vaccines for humans was the influenza vaccine developed by Thomas Francis and Jonas Salk in 1943.

To attenuate a live virus means to weaken it so that it will produce only mild symptoms. The general procedure is to cultivate the virus for many generations—usually in cells which the virus does not normally attack—until a mild strain of the virus is produced. For example, white mice were infected with yellow fever viruses taken from a human patient who died of the disease. The new environment favored the survival of mutant strains of the virus which could not have lasted in the human body. Eventually a strain was found which conferred immunity on man but produced no illness at all.

The chick embryo has been a standard laboratory tool since 1931, when Ernest W. Goodpasture and Alice M. Woodruff worked out techniques for its use in the cultivation of viruses. Before that time, only two human antivirus vaccines had been developed: Jenner's smallpox vaccine in 1798 and Pasteur's rabies vaccine in 1885.

The virologist needs a manageable laboratory animal on which he can experiment, and from which he can gather enough virus to make a vaccine in quantity. Jenner had found a ready-made vaccine in the cow, and Pasteur had made his vaccine by passing the rabies virus through a long line of rabbits. But other "human" viruses were extremely particular about which cells they chose to multiply in; virologists were severely hampered in their work with vaccines until the viruses were introduced to the unborn chick.

Another giant step was taken in 1949 when John F. Enders, Thomas H. Weller and Frederick C. Robbins succeeded in cultivating polio viruses in ordinary tissue cultures of non-nervous tissue. Human

tissues could be kept alive in test tubes, and viruses could be kept multiplying in the tissues. The mass production of viruses in tissue cultures is common practice today and is often accomplished with the aid of roller tubes. The sealed tubes in this photograph are being used to cultivate polio virus. They are held in cylindrical racks which rotate slowly so that the tissues in the tubes will be alternately exposed to air and bathed in a nutrient solution.

The production of live-virus vaccines would be impossible if viruses did not mutate and thus produce new strains with properties different from the fully infectious parent virus.

But the ability to mutate is of great advantage to the virus as well as to the virologist. A virus which can mutate to produce milder strains can also mutate to produce more virulent strains. Furthermore, a virus can mutate to produce a new strain which is no longer vulnerable to the blocking action of existing antibodies; such a mutation, of course, renders an established immunity obsolete.

The influenza pandemic of 1918 and the more recent and milder epidemics of Asian flu are both examples of virus mutants that bypassed the antibodies effective against earlier strains of the virus. The influenza virus and many of the viruses responsible for the common cold are particularly "unstable," and they mutate more readily than the average virus.

As a consequence of such dynamic variety among virus strains, the task of making new vaccines to combat virus disease can never be completed, even theoretically. The virologist will continue to look for mutant strains of viruses which can be used as vaccines, and the viruses will continue to produce mutants which are indifferent to whatever vaccines man may have devised.

How a Virus Gets Around

THE VIRUS has absolutely no powers of locomotion, yet it is one of the best-traveled creatures—or non-creatures—on earth.

Viruses travel by air, land and sea. They travel by plane and by insect, and they fly alone on the wind. They travel by bird and by boat, by worm and by fish.

Not only are viruses committed to traveling; they *must* travel if they are to survive. Any virus imprisoned within the plant or animal it has killed is as good as dead itself. It must get to other susceptible plants or animals in order to multiply; and if it does not multiply it will remain less than a speck of dust forever.

There is little danger of such an unglamorous end, however. The helpless virus is obligingly transported by its victims, who eat it up, sneeze it out, carry it away or fly off with it.

Measles, polio and the pox viruses are usually transferred from man to man by close contact, sneezing, or coughing. Once inside a new host, they still have to find susceptible cells. This is not difficult, for they are circulated along with blood or lymph, or perhaps they spread along nerve fibers.

In the vegetable world, viruses enter plants through breaks and bruises, or they may be inoculated into plant cells by boring insects. Once inside, they spread from cell to cell and are carried throughout the plant by flowing sap.

The least dignified form of transport is reserved for the bacterial viruses, which for the most part are merely kicked about by the random bombardment of much smaller molecules.

At the opposite extreme are the viruses which have profited from the invention of the airplane. The Asian flu virus, for example, first appeared as a new, unique strain in southwestern China; within a few months it had been spread throughout the world by man and his flying machine.

The rabies virus is somewhat more prosaic since it is commonly spread by land-bound rodents; however, it is also carried by bats.

Insects suffer from virus diseases, but they are better known as the "common carriers" of many viruses that attack animals and of practically all plant viruses. Lice, ticks, flies, aphids and mosquitoes all assure the transmission of viruses from plant to plant or from animal to animal. Even a single insect may keep a virus going; when a mosquito bites a man suffering from yellow fever or dengue fever, it is capable of ingesting as many as a million viruses at a single feeding.

A tiny green plant louse called Myzus persicae transmits at least 50 different plant viruses, including those causing disease in potatoes, beans, cabbages, onions, tulips and sugar beets.

Some viruses are spread from host to host in a much more roundabout way. The WEE virus (the virus causing the western form of equine encephalitis) infects chickens and wild birds, but these hosts show no signs of disease. Mites carry the virus from fowl to fowl, and this cycle insures a dependable reservoir of viruses. Sporadically, the virus infects men or horses, and it also infects mosquitoes that feed on the fowl.

The most famous case of complicated hitchhiking among viruses is that worked out by Dr. Richard E. Shope of the Rockefeller Institute. It concerns the swine influenza virus, found in the lungs of pigs. Lungworms in the pig's lungs take in the viruses and may keep them for years. But the viruses also find their way into the lungworm's eggs. Inside the eggs, the viruses are carried to the outside world by way of the pig's intestinal tract. Earthworms eat the lungworm eggs, which then proceed to hatch inside the earthworms. The lungworm larvae, still containing the viruses, develop as parasites of the earthworms.

Finally, the earthworms are eaten by a pig. The immature lungworms are freed from inside the earthworms and migrate to the pig's lungs, where they become adult lungworms and pass the viruses on to the pig. In short, the pig eats earthworms infested with lungworms infected with viruses which came from a pig.

The only example of virus transportation that might be considered more remarkable is the case of the virus that reverses its passive role and becomes a carrier instead of a passenger. In this instance, a physically helpless virus manages to take an important piece of genetic material from the nucleus of a cell and carry it intact into the nucleus of another cell. This strange process—transduction—is discussed in detail in the following chapter. It might possibly explain the spread of some cancers from cell to cell.

CANCER IS A disease in which cells reproduce too readily.

There are many kinds of cancers, including hundreds that affect plants and animals and more than 250 that thrive in man. They kill some 250,000 Americans each year; they account for 10,000 new cases of cancer every week; and they all have one characteristic in common: they are made of cells which can multiply without limit and which can pass this ability on to all of their progeny.

Cancer begins when an apparently normal cell in any tissue of the body undergoes a change which causes it to reproduce wildly. The cell also may become altered in shape or size or function, and every such abnormality is also passed on from generation to generation.

Cancerous tissue is marked not by the great speed with which the cells multiply but by the fact that cell reproduction is uncontrolled. Some normal tissues—regenerating liver, for example—can grow more rapidly than most cancers, but all normal cells stop multiplying when the tissue has attained its characteristic size and shape.

The abnormal growth typical of cancer can be seen in this specimen of a cancer of the colon. Between normal tissue at either end of the microscope slide is a bulky tumor.

The problem of curing cancer can be stated in the form of two general questions:

What causes normal cells to change into cancerous cells?
How can we inhibit or reverse this change without damaging normal cells at the same time?

Whatever may be involved in the transformation of a normal into a cancerous cell, we know that this change is hereditary; it is perpetuated in all the progeny of the altered cell. Therefore, it must involve initially a change in the hereditary material of the cell—the chromosomes.

The most obvious way to change chromosomes is to damage them physically. This can be accomplished with radiation, either natural or man-made; and we know that heavy doses of radiation can lead to cancer.

These two photomicrographs of cells of the wake-robin plant, Trillium erectum, provide a beautiful example of what radiation can do to chromosomes. In both pictures the cell is about to divide and the chromosomes are clearly visible. The only difference between the two is that the cell above is normal while the one below has been exposed to X rays. Some of the irradiated chromosomes have been broken, disoriented or stretched into chromosome "bridges."

The structure—and therefore also the function—of chromosomes can be changed by many other means, including the action of drugs and infection of the cell by a virus. The problem is to determine precisely which agents or processes are responsible for the changes that lead to cancer.

A vast amount of research has been focused upon this problem recently and a number of different approaches to it have been investigated. The research we shall discuss here is that which is concerned with the role of the virus.

In 1903, a few years after the discovery of the first virus, the French bacteriologist, Amédée Borrel, suggested that viruses might have something to do with cancer. But his suggestion apparently was not taken seriously.

Five years later in Denmark, Wilhelm Ellerman and Olaf Bang proved that fowl leukemia was caused by a virus. Their proof did not

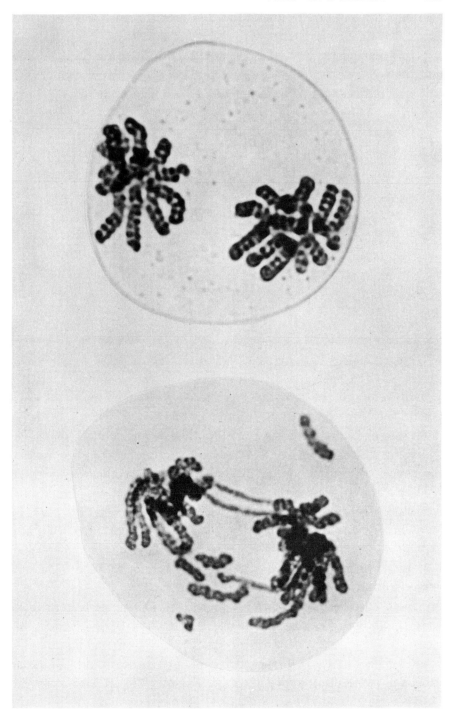

lend support to Borrel's suggestion, however, because leukemia was not at that time considered a malignant disease.

It remained for Peyton Rous, in 1911, to discover the first sure link between viruses and cancer. Dr. Rous, who was working with chickens, noticed a growth similar to the one pictured here.

He removed the growth from the chicken and found that cells taken from this cancer would reproduce the cancer when inoculated into other chickens. Then, as Dr. Rubin has pointed out, he made the surprising discovery that an extract from the tumor would reproduce the cancer even after he had passed it through a filter designed to hold back the smallest germ. The cancer, a natural disease of chickens, was obviously caused by a virus.

This "Rous sarcoma" virus has been the object of intensive study ever since. One significant finding was that this virus is quite specific; that is, it decidedly prefers chicken cells, although it also can be adapted to turkeys and pheasants.

Such specificity later proved to be a common characteristic of most tumor viruses. Perhaps the best example is that of the virus causing cancer in the kidneys of the leopard frog. Balduin Lucké, who studied this virus in the 1930's, noted that it would not cause cancer in some other types of frogs. Even in the leopard frog, the virus always migrated to the kidneys; no matter where the frog was inoculated—skin, muscle or abdominal cavity—the cancer showed up only in the kidneys.

Richard E. Shope found a virus that causes papillomas, or warts, on wild rabbits; and subsequent investigations revealed that these benign warts usually developed into malignant cancers.

Another virus causing cancer in animals was discovered by John Bittner at the Jackson Laboratory in Maine. This was the mouse mammary cancer virus, transmitted from mother to offspring through the mother's milk. The virus seems to remain in a more or less latent form for several months, but great breast tumors form when the mouse gets older.

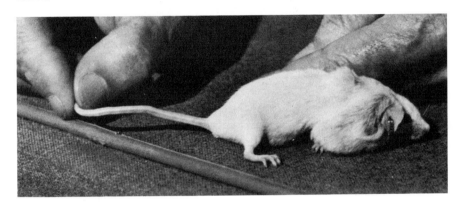

This virus-induced cancer, a natural disease of the mouse, is particularly interesting because the activity of the virus is greatly affected by the mouse's genetic background and the activity of her hormones. By selective breeding and control of hormones, the susceptibility of the mice can be raised to 100 per cent, or lowered to less than 10 per cent.

One of the most potent and versatile of the known causes of cancer is the recently discovered polyoma ("many-tumor") virus, the first cancer virus to cause the disease in more than one type of animal. It produces multiple tumors in mice, rats and hamsters; these tumors come in more than three dozen varieties, and they occur in a large number of different bodily organs. Polyoma is also the first virus found to cause cancer by virtue of its nucleic acid alone; hamsters inoculated with polyoma nucleic acid, minus the viral protein, develop characteristic tumors.

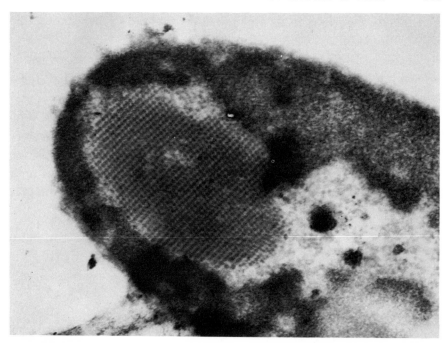

This electron micrograph shows a polyoma virus crystal embedded in the nucleus of a cell from a culture of embryonic mouse tissue. The polyoma crystal, like the tobacco mosaic virus crystal on page 20, is an "inclusion body," an aggregate of viruses walled off inside a cell. The magnification is 75,000 diameters.

Other viruses have been found to cause cancer in ducks, cats, dogs, horses, cows, deer and many other animals. Even plants are subject to cancer-like growths caused by viruses.

Despite the evidence that viruses can cause cancer in animals, many researchers have been reluctant until recently to admit that viruses might have anything to do with cancer in humans.

It is true that no evidence was uncovered before about 1960 to indicate that human cancer might be infectious. But in general, basic biological processes do not differ very much within the cells of different species of animals; therefore, the findings in regard to animal cancer viruses appear to be directly pertinent to the human cancer problem. We would do well to assume that viruses *are* responsible for most kinds of cancer and then proceed to design and execute experiments to test this assumption.

The failure to find a human cancer virus could be due to very low concentrations of virus particles in diseased tissues. This possibility can now be investigated, thanks to new procedures which should serve quite well to concentrate human cancer viruses and convert them from an apparently noninfectious state to a condition in which their activity can be measured.

Until a very few years ago, the investigation of human cancer viruses was seriously hampered by the fact that viruses cannot be tested on human beings as they can on mice. Mice are of little help in this case because viruses will cause disease only in specific cells of specific animals; a mouse is no substitute for a man, even from the point of view of a virus.

This roadblock has now been eliminated by the development of techniques for growing a variety of isolated human tissues in the laboratory. One of the most helpful of these tissues is the amnion, the membrane surrounding a baby at birth. Elsa Zitcer of the University of California found that the human amnion can be grown in tissue culture and successfully infected with viruses.

It was also found by Dr. Jorgen Fogh that uninfected amnion cells grown in the laboratory often begin to look like cancer cells after a certain number of generations. This gives us an opportunity to study a transformation of normal human cells into cells having certain malignant properties.

Now that virologists have been alerted to the possibility that human cancer may be caused by viruses, and now that new techniques for working with such potential human cancer viruses are available, it may seem strange that no one has discovered such a virus. Actually, we already may have discovered a human cancer virus without knowing it. More than 200 new viruses have been isolated from man since 1955, and in many cases a given virus has not yet been identified with any known disease.

During the past few years there has been a surge of interest in the possible relationships between viruses and human cancer. Many laboratories are attempting to isolate potential human tumor viruses.

Leon Dmochowski of the University of Texas has made electron micrographs comparing virus particles known to cause leukemia in mice with particles suspected of causing leukemia in man. Leukemia is a fatal disease involving tremendous overproduction of immature white blood cells.

The picture on the left shows characteristic particles in the lymph node of a mouse infected with mouse leukemia viruses. The second picture shows a section of a lymph node of a young girl who died of human leukemia. The similarity of the two groups of particles is striking.

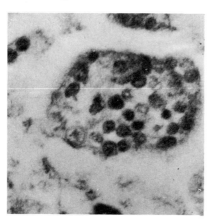 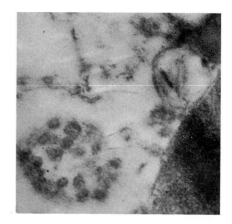

We do not know that the particles on the right have anything to do with leukemia. It would have to be proven beyond a reasonable doubt that the particles actually are viruses and that they are the agents which caused the cancer.

In 1960, Dr. Steven O. Schwartz obtained evidence indicating that extracts from the brains of human leukemia victims contain a virus causing leukemia. Dr. Schwartz reported that men inoculated with such extracts develop protective antibodies against the virus.

Although human cancers do not appear to be infectious, it is quite possible for appearances to deceive. Bacterial viruses, for example, sometimes operate without exhibiting the usual signs of infection. The bacteriophage may undergo a slight change which allows it to exist inside a bacterial cell in a latent form. Instead of producing 200 or 300 copies of itself, the phage simply duplicates itself once every time the cell divides. This intimate coexistence of virus and cell is known as lysogeny. It may continue for generations and produce many thriving bacteria, each containing a single "hidden" virus. The concealed virus can be brought out into the open, however, by treating the bacterium with X rays or with certain chemicals. When this is done, the virus springs into action, producing several hundred copies of itself and killing its host.

A similar process seems to occur among certain mice infected with leukemia viruses. Careful examination of the mice reveals nothing to indicate the presence of a virus. Yet, as Ludwig Gross and Henry Kaplan discovered, the mice develop leukemia when they are given a light "treatment" with X rays. Viruses now can be found in the sick mice, and these viruses will cause leukemia when inoculated into a healthy mouse.

There are many examples of latent viruses that may remain hidden for a lifetime or even for generations, only to come to light as the result of some treatment or change. And our knowledge of such lysogenic relationships is consistent with the possibility that a cancer virus could exist in man without being detected.

Another process which suggests a possible unobserved relationship between viruses and human cancer is that of transduction. In 1952, Norton D. Zinder and Joshua Lederberg discovered that genetic information could be carried by viruses from one type of Salmonella bacteria to another type. The virus infects one type of bacterium and—perhaps after a period of lysogenic cohabitation with the cell—multiplies normally. But one or more of the resulting progeny carries away with it a fragment of a bacterial chromosome. The "carrier" virus eventually infects a bacterium of a different type and adds to it the stolen chromosome fragment. The newly infected bacterium thus acquires a new hereditary characteristic.

To explain this process schematically, we can design two idealized bacteria which are clearly distinguishable. The first bacterium

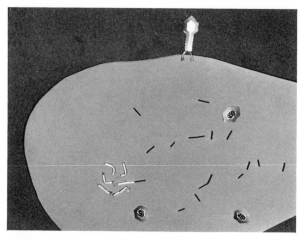

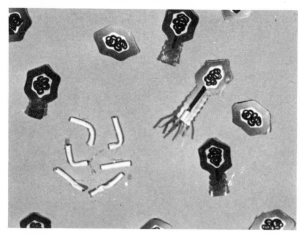

is egg-shaped and has white chromosomes. The second bacterium is shaped like a potato and has striped chromosomes.

A bacterial virus, the bacteriophage T2, for example, infects the first bacterium by injecting its nucleic acid.

Once inside the bacterium, the viral nucleic acid begins to multiply, making a large number of copies of itself.

One of the newly made nucleic acid strands, however, gets tangled up with the chromosomes of the bacterium; it becomes attached to a small piece of one of the chromosomes, a piece which happens to control the bacterium's outward shape.

Coats of viral protein begin to gather around each of the nucleic acid strands, building complete new virus particles. The "carrier" virus we're interested in also receives a protein coat, but it differs from all the other new viruses because it has incorporated the white bacterial chromosome fragment along with its own nucleic acid.

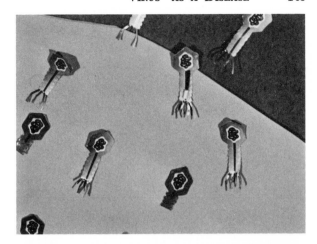

All of the new viruses eventually break out of the bacterium and disperse. We follow our "carrier" virus until, in due time, it infects another bacterium. But this second bacterium is of a different strain; it is shaped like a potato, and it has striped chromosomes. It also has a different effect on the virus. The viral nucleic acid does not destroy this bacterium; instead, it attaches itself to the bacterium's chromo-

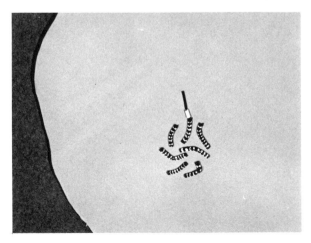

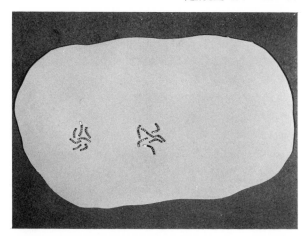

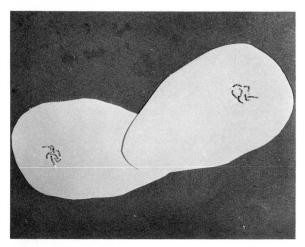

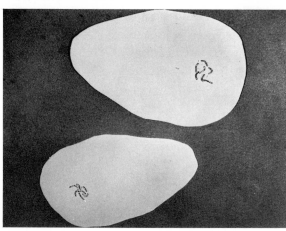

somes. In so doing, it deposits the bit of white chromosome originally obtained from the now-deceased, egg-shaped bacterium.

These chromosomes now possess a trait they never had before.

Whenever the striped bacterial chromosomes duplicate themselves preparatory to the reproduction of the entire cell, the newly acquired bit of white chromosome is duplicated along with them.

Furthermore, since this white chromosome fragment contains directions for making *egg*-shaped bacteria, the resulting daughter cells are shaped like eggs and not like potatoes.

This new shape is henceforth passed on to all descendants of the "transduced" bacterium. The chromosomes of all the progeny are still for the most part striped, and are descended from the true parent. The shape, however, comes from a stranger by courtesy of a virus.

In actual experiments, Dr. Zinder and Dr. Lederberg were able to transduce many different traits, ranging from drug resistance to swimming ability, from one bacterium to another by way of a virus. Only a few of the bacteria in a single culture will gain new traits by transduction, but once a bacterium has incorporated the genetic "instructions" for some new property, the change becomes permanent.

If transduction should prove to be possible in the case of human beings, then the hundreds of viruses that constantly travel from person to person would represent a significant means of transferring genetic material in the cells of man. And if such genetic material should by chance include the trait of generating malignant growth in human cells, we should have to label human cancer an infectious disease. The fact that transduction actually occurs on a random basis only about once for every 100,000 virus transmissions could explain why infectiousness is neither apparent nor easy to demonstrate in man.

Aside from the question of cancer, the fact that man carries so many viruses within his cells and that these are continually passing from person to person means that we should always remain alert to the possibility of transduction by these viruses.

Both lysogeny and transduction emphasize the similarity of viruses to the chromosome fragments we call genes. In lysogeny, the virus becomes an integral part of the bacterial chromosome; we could just as well say that the chromosome has simply acquired a new trait, the ability to make an infectious virus upon demand. In transduction, part of the chromosome breaks out of the bacterium, travels as an independent unit and then "infects" a new bacterial cell.

The lysogenic virus acts like a gene and the transduced chromosome fragment acts like a virus. We hardly know which to call "virus" and which to call "gene" for it is obvious that at times the two merge completely.

Returning to the more immediate prospects of research into the relationship of viruses to cancer, a number of different approaches are being investigated.

The study of enzyme production in the living cell, for example, has led to the discovery of an intriguing parallel between the behavior of the cell during cancerous growth and the behavior of the cell during the production of viruses. The number of cell enzymes regulating sugar production increases when the cell is infected by a virus; this in turn increases the cell's output of energy, which becomes available for the manufacture of virus nucleoprotein. This complex and abnormal process closely resembles what goes on in the cell during the wild growth of cancerous tissues.

Virologists at the Sloan-Kettering Institute have recently established that inoculation with cancerous cells apparently can create immunity to cancer in man. Whether or not immunity might be caused by viruses inside the cells remains an open question. However, if we do discover that viruses are responsible for human cancer, we can take hope from the fact that successful vaccines have recently been developed for virus-induced cancers in animals.

The prospect of using viruses as a weapon *against* cancer has been investigated by Robert Huebner and others at the National Institutes of Health. Huebner discovered that adenoviruses would destroy the abnormal cells of cervical cancer in women. Inoculation of these viruses into a cervical cancer mass or into the blood stream resulted in the disintegration and disappearance of most of the cancerous tissue. However, the virus could not destroy all the cancer cells before antibodies to the virus developed. These antibodies inactivated the "invading" virus and thus served to protect the residual cancer.

Work of this general nature is only in its infancy, but it is most significant that infection of certain cancer cells with certain viruses will destroy the cancer cells. By selective cultivation of mutant virus strains, it should be possible to develop viruses which ignore normal cells but will have a special predilection for the destruction of cancer cells.

Since 1920, extensive studies have been made on chemical carcinogens, or cancer-inducers, and it has long been known that cancer could result from prolonged exposure to coal tar. It is generally assumed that the carcinogen provokes some change in normal cells, causing them to progress to cancer. However, a few investigators have suggested that the chemical carcinogen works by activating a latent virus or by causing a latent virus to mutate.

That a latent virus could persist in man for many years, for a lifetime, or even for two or more generations, is not unexpected or unusual. It is in complete accord with well-established biological principles.

A most pertinent fact to remember at this point is that certain lysogenic strains of bacteria will break open and release hundreds of virus particles after the bacteria have been treated with physical or chemical agents such as X rays or nitrogen mustard. Some of these agents, or inducers, have long been recognized as cancer-inducing agents for man and animals.

Is it possible that activation of a latent virus by such "inducers" could provide a model of a process occurring in man?

We know that man has coursing through his body many viruses which were unknown a few years ago, and we do not know what many of these are doing there. We know that viruses can persist in a host for generations, in either an infectious or noninfectious form. We know that viruses can mutate to form new strains which cause different disease symptoms. We know that viruses may have different effects depending upon age, genetics, and the state of nutrition and hormonal balance of the host. We know that different carcinogenic agents can activate latent viruses, with consequent destruction of the cells. And finally, we know that viruses can cause cancer.

It would certainly appear that the activation of latent viruses, as well as the phenomenon of transduction, is pertinent to the human cancer problem.

It is difficult to escape the conclusion that viruses may be the causative agents for most, if not all, cancer, including cancer in man, and that this represents by far the most intellectually satisfying working hypothesis consistent with all presently known facts.

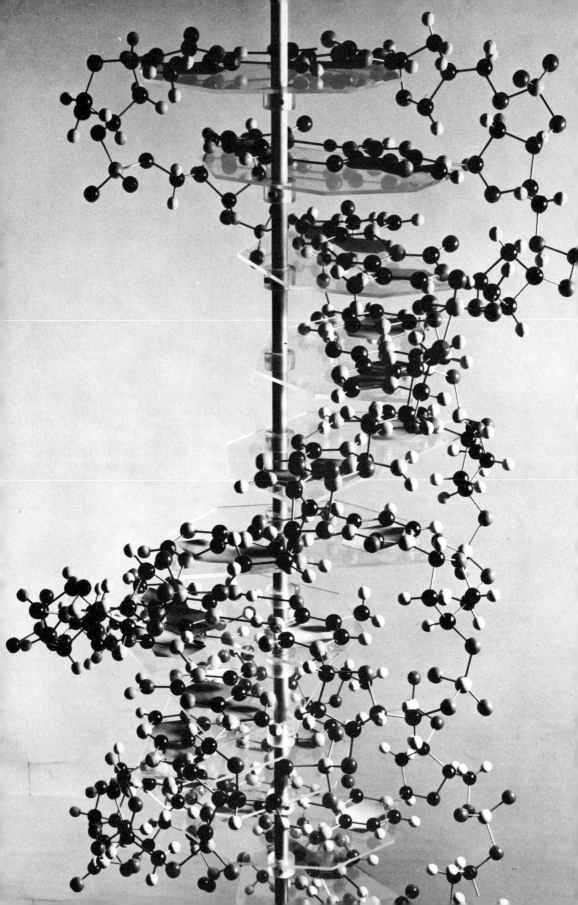

THE CHEMICALS OF LIFE

THE VITAL ELEMENTS

EVERYTHING ON earth is composed of one or more of the 103 chemical elements.

The great bulk of this material is tied up more or less permanently in the form of very simple compounds like silica and other oxides which constitute rock.

But we are interested in the elements of which living things are made and in the way these elements are fitted together to form organic compounds. These organic compounds may be extremely complex, as we can see in this model of a very small fragment of a DNA molecule.

What are the "elements of life"?

If we analyze a man into his constituent atoms, we find that he is composed principally of the following elements: oxygen (65% by weight), carbon (18%), hydrogen (10%), nitrogen (3%), calcium (2%), and phosphorus (1%). He also contains small amounts of potassium, sulfur, sodium, chlorine, magnesium, and iron, plus traces of iodine, fluorine and silicon.

We could guess from this merely quantitative analysis that the most important elements in man are oxygen, carbon, hydrogen and nitrogen; therefore, it is not surprising to find that these are the principal atomic building blocks of both proteins and nucleic acids. Nucleic acid also contains phosphorus; some proteins also contain sulfur.

Nucleic acid and protein form the substance of viruses and of the genetic material, or chromosomes, in all living things. Protein alone is the basic structural material in man and other animals.

We have now narrowed our list of elements down to six: oxygen, carbon, hydrogen and nitrogen, plus phosphorus in the case of nucleic acid and sulfur in the case of protein. These six are the

151

vital elements of life in both the chemical and general senses of the word.

Which of these six is the *most* vital?

This is a naïve question insofar as any one element is of no significance without the others, but there is still merit in the question. Since water accounts for 60 to 70 per cent of man's weight, not much of the oxygen and hydrogen in man are left for the formation of proteins and nucleic acids. This puts carbon very much at the head of our list of vital elements; carbon accounts for more than half of man's dry weight.

Is there any particular explanation for this emphasis on carbon? Yes. The explanation is to be found in the structure of the carbon atom, which is important enough to warrant a short review of its well-known but unusual properties.

The nucleus of the carbon atom contains six positive electric charges. The atom has two electrons, or negative charges, in an inner orbit, and four more electrons in its outer shell, as illustrated in this schematic diagram.

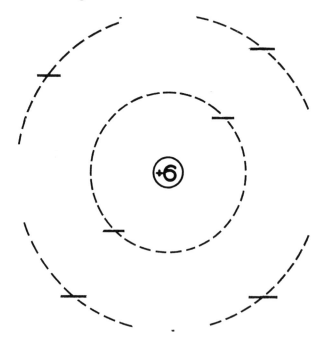

These four outer electrons are located in a shell which could contain up to eight electrons, as in the case of the neon atom.

An atom like neon is chemically inert because its outer shell contains all the electrons it can possibly hold; none is left over to form attachments with other atoms, and there is no gap in the shell into which electrons of other atoms might fit. Chemical activity always depends upon the number of "extra" electrons in an atom's outer shell or upon the number of gaps where electrons are "missing" from the shell.

In its chemical activity, carbon is somewhat like a metal because of its "extra" electrons and yet like a halogen (fluorine, for example) because of the "gaps" in its outer electron shell.

Whether it behaves like a metal or like a halogen, the carbon atom has four points of attachment by which it can bind itself to other atoms.

This unique property of carbon makes it possible for the atom to combine readily with other atoms in a variety of ways, and it accounts for the fact that carbon is a constituent of some 500,000 known chemical compounds.

The carbon atom is traditionally represented as a "C" with four short lines to indicate its points of attachment to other atoms.

Atoms are usually held together by a single one of these "bonds," but they may also be joined by double or triple bonds. For example, carbon may employ single, double or triple bonds when it combines with hydrogen as it does in the case of methane (CH_4), ethylene (C_2H_4), or acetylene (C_2H_2).

Nitrogen commonly has three bonds available for chemical combinations. Oxygen has two, and hydrogen one.

Is it possible to determine how the six kinds of atoms in a simple virus like TMV are linked together? In view of the fact that a single TMV particle contains about 5,250,000 individual atoms which could be joined together in an almost infinite number of ways, the problem appears insoluble.

But fortunately there is a great deal of simplicity hidden in this complexity. Viruses are constructed in a very orderly manner. Nucleic acid is anything but a haphazard rope of atoms, and viral protein is not something which can be smeared casually onto the outside of a virus.

A TMV particle is a nucleoprotein, and it can be broken apart into a nucleic acid segment and a protein segment. The general structure of both protein and nucleic acid is that of a high polymer, a single molecule formed when a string of similar small molecules is bound together as a unit.

The protein can be divided into some 2,200 identical subunits, each one of which is a smaller protein molecule. The subunits can be further divided into roughly similar structures called amino acid residues, many of which are identical with one another. And finally these can be broken down into their constituent atoms.

In a somewhat similar manner, the nucleic acid of the virus can be subdivided. The RNA of tobacco mosaic virus is a long molecule made of only four different kinds of structures called nucleotides. There are some 6,500 nucleotides in the entire molecule, and they are strung together like beads. Each nucleotide can be divided into three characteristic parts, two of which are identical among all the nucleotides, regardless of their type. And again, these smaller units are divisible into atoms.

Why should we be so interested in the chemical make-up of a virus? The main reason is that viruses are closely related in structure and function to the chromosomes of living cells. Both are nucleoproteins, composite molecules found exclusively in chromosomes and viruses. Both are able to control their duplication so as to make exact replicas of themselves. And they are so similar in chemical structure that the nucleic acid molecule of the virus is able to substitute itself for part of the nucleic acid in the cell.

The viral nucleic acid acts as part of the cell and determines how the cell will function and what products it will manufacture. Yet it is a part of the cell that is independent and able to come out into the open where it can be studied. This aspect of viruses is what makes them so valuable to biologists; they offer a unique opportunity to observe in isolation the structures responsible for making every cell the *particular* cell that it is.

As we learn more about how a virus is built and how its parts are put together, we come closer to an explanation of reproduction in chemical terms; this, in turn, is leading us to an understanding of the specific kinds of chemical and physical forces which induce mutation and the kinds of misfunctions responsible for cancer.

One example of the great practical importance of such understanding is that chemists have now learned how to make synthetic nucleotides which cancerous cells will incorporate. These synthetic nucleic acid fragments are subtly altered forms; they do not quite fit properly into the reproductive machinery of the cancerous cells and they eventually jam this machinery, changing or destroying the cells.

Under special laboratory conditions, such "fraudulent" nucleotides have been able to destroy cancer cells without harming normal cells. Thus we have direct evidence that it might be possible to use synthetic chemicals for the selective destruction of cancerous tissue.

In general, what we are learning about the way nucleoproteins are built enables us to appreciate in a new light the potentialities inherent in chemical structure. We are beginning to understand what a specific known difference in chemical structure means in terms of how a cell will grow and reproduce itself.

THERE ARE hundreds of thousands of differents kinds of protein in living things. Protein comes in forms as various as silk, fingernails, skin, hormones, enzymes, peanuts and viruses. Gelatin, egg albumin, pepsin, casein and insulin are pure protein, and viruses may be up to 95 per cent protein. Some 50,000 different kinds of protein account for nearly half of the dry weight of the human body.

Yet every protein molecule consists of one or more long sequences of amino acids—only 20 different kinds at most—locked together like links in a chain.

How can 20 molecular units in various combinations account for the many thousands of different kinds of protein that we know?

A rough answer is that each kind of protein molecule has a characteristic way of reacting chemically with other substances; and it has a characteristic shape which is determined by the way in which the long chain of amino acids is bent and coiled over on itself. These characteristics, in turn, are due simply to the relative amounts of the various amino acids and their particular sequence; that is, they are due to the chemical structure of the protein molecule.

In order to see what it takes to make a protein, we can return to our old standby, the tobacco mosaic virus.

No one has ever seen a close-up of a TMV particle, and the models we have made of the virus are at best only models; they illustrate in a rather symbolic form some of the facts gleaned from chemical, X-ray and other studies.

The 2,200 or so protein subunits of TMV, for example, are not really very much like the smooth, white, pontoon-shaped objects in the model. If we could observe them in much more detail, we would see each subunit as a long coiled strand doubled up on itself.

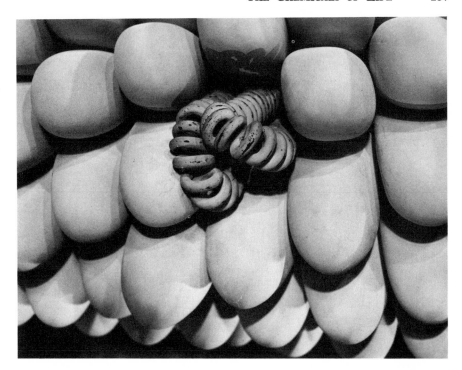

This coiled and doubly folded strand assumes a very precise form, however, and its gross shape is very much like that of the other subunits in the model. Every subunit is coiled and folded in exactly the same way, and every one becomes an individual protein molecule when separated from its neighbors.

Any subunit can be unfolded and uncoiled by chemical treatment. Such treatment breaks the relatively weak bonds that hold the molecule in its characteristic shape and allows it to stretch out into a long straight strand. This strand is still a protein molecule, although some of its properties have been destroyed by the stretching process. It is composed of a long line of amino acid "residues" and is called an amino acid chain, or a polypeptide.

An amino acid residue is simply an amino acid that has lost one oxygen and two hydrogen atoms.

An amino acid is an acid containing what is called an amino group—a combination of a nitrogen and two hydrogen atoms. It consists of a string of four atoms (oxygen-carbon-carbon-nitrogen), each of which is linked with an atom of hydrogen or an atom of oxygen.

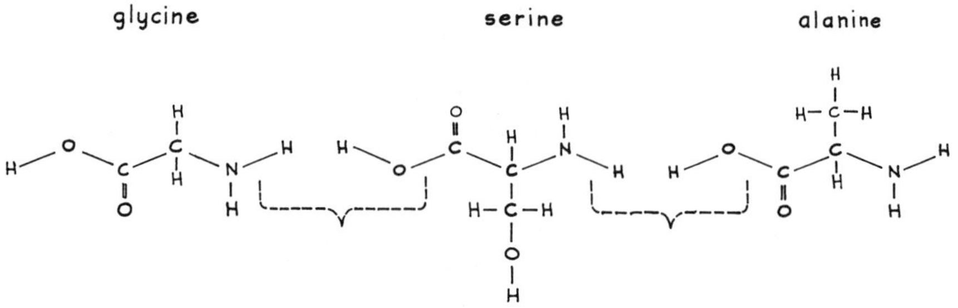

glycine   serine   alanine

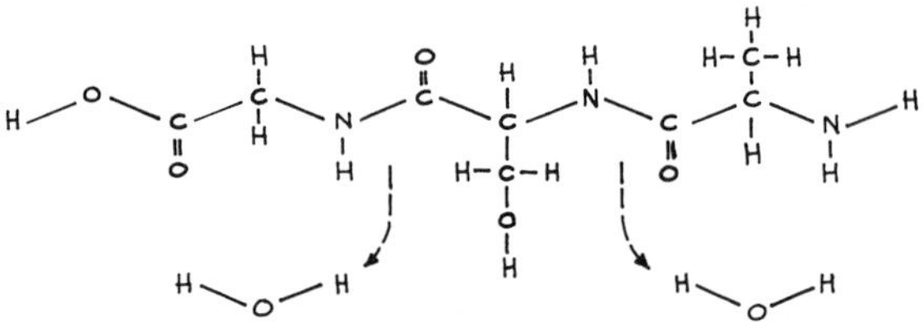

To one of the carbons is attached a group of atoms which distinguishes one amino acid from another.

More than 20 amino acids are known, and the simplest of these is glycine. It consists of only 10 atoms and is distinguished from other amino acids by one of the hydrogen atoms attached to the central carbon atom. Each of the other amino acids has a relatively complex group of atoms in place of glycine's one hydrogen.

When amino acids are strung together, each one loses an atom of hydrogen from one end and a hydrogen and an oxygen atom from the other end. The result is a polypeptide plus water.

The diagram above represents a *tripeptide* made from glycine, serine and alanine. It has a "backbone" of repeated CO—CH—NH units.

A more likely tripeptide is the lysine-tyrosine-leucine combination on the facing page. It could represent a segment of the 158-unit polypeptide which comprises the protein of some strains of tobacco mosaic virus. Matching the diagram is a molecular model in which each small sphere represents an atom. The "backbone" is shown in black while the three dissimilar side groups are shown in white. The model illustrates roughly what a very short piece of TMV protein might look like if we could see its atomic structure.

leucine

tyrosine

lysine

The same tripeptide can be illustrated in a simpler symbolic form with paper cutouts. Again, black represents the CO–CH–NH "backbone" of the molecule and white the side groups.

Pictured in the same way, a section of a much larger polypeptide would look like the string of subunits in the lower photograph.

Such an extended polypeptide can be broken into fragments; each fragment will itself be a polypeptide molecule with properties different from other fragments and different from the original.

The fragments on the opposite page are those which would result from the destructive action of the enzyme, trypsin, which is itself a protein molecule. Trypsin breaks a chain of amino acids on one side of every lysine and arginine unit in the chain.

The distinctive properties of a particular protein—the way it looks and feels, the way it responds to heat, the way it reacts with other molecules—are determined by its structure. This structure, in turn, is a reflection of the number, the relative amounts, and the sequence of the amino acid residues in the molecule.

Since there are at least two points on every amino acid where a chemical bond may be formed, the

simplest way for the units to join together is in the form of a chain.
However, some amino acids have
three or more places at which they
can be attached to other units. Consequently, units which are at some
distance from one another *along* the
chain may stick together when the
chain folds back upon itself. The
result is a molecule resembling a ball
of sticky thread, except that the
threads of every molecule of a particular protein are kinked, coiled,
bent and linked in precisely the
same way.

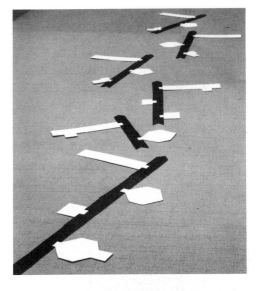

Polypeptides range in size from short proteins like vasopressin,
which constricts a bull's blood vessels and which contains nine amino
acid units, to long chains like ovalbumin, the principal protein of
egg white, containing 400 units.

There are so many possible combinations of the 20 amino acid
residues that a different combination could easily be designed for
every grain of sand on earth and every drop of water in the oceans.
The 158 amino acid units in TMV protein are listed on page 212.

A class of molecules allowing such variety and versatility certainly merits the label *protein,* a name derived from the Greek word
proteios, which means "of the first rank."

Viruses are built largely of protein, of course, but they are also
intimately involved with other proteins, notably with enzymes and
antibodies.

Enzymes are protein molecules which act as biological catalysts.
They are essential to all living processes, and their function is to
speed up the rate of the various chemical reactions which support life
in all its forms. Enzymes digest food, draw power from oxygen, and
deliver energy to muscles. They break up large and small molecules,
including proteins, and they enable amino acids to combine to form
new proteins; enzymes even make enzymes.

A specific enzyme can perform only one specific task, but it can repeat this task thousands of times every minute. Complex chemical reactions proceed step by step as a series of co-ordinated simple reactions, and each step requires a different enzyme.

Viruses, insofar as they display any of the characteristics of living things, are utterly dependent upon the activity of enzymes. Enzymes are needed to break into a cell, to carry out the production of new viruses, and then to break out of the exhausted cell. A minute or two after the virus has infected a bacterium, for example, a new enzyme appears which can synthesize a needed compound from material inside the cell. Soon, at least 10 other enzymes are busy breaking up unwanted cellular components and putting together new viruses.

Viruses are also dependent—in a thoroughly negative way—upon the activity of another class of proteins, the antibodies.

An antibody is a molecule that circulates in the blood serum and can react with and inactivate some specific foreign substance, which is called an antigen. An antigen, in turn, is defined as a substance which stimulates the production of a particular antibody when introduced into an animal. The antibody-antigen reaction occurs when the two combine with one another.

Most proteins are good antigens, and the protein coat of a virus is no exception. Consequently, infection of an animal by a virus causes the animal to produce antibodies; and as soon as enough antibodies have been made, they protect the animal against further invasion by this particular virus. Thus the animal, if it lives, becomes immune.

Antivirus vaccines, of course, operate on the same principle. In a killed-virus vaccine, the viral nucleic acid is unable to cause disease. In a live-virus vaccine, the virulence of the nucleic acid has been bred out of the virus by the cultivation of weakened strains. In either case, the viral protein maintains its ability to stimulate the production of antibodies and thus protect us against infection.

However, this protection is effective only because the antibodies in a immune person react with the specific protein of a specific virus. If the virus mutates in such a way as to change the composition of its protein—by altering the sequence of amino acids in the protein, for instance—then the antibodies will no longer have any effect on the virus. Thus, when a new strain of influenza virus appears, existing vaccines offer no protection against it.

The protein of a virus is also important in another way: its chemical structure is probably the factor that determines the kinds of organisms and the kinds of cells the virus is able to attack. A specific protein will attach itself only to a very limited variety of cells; all other cells are essentially immune.

Nucleic acid, the relatively fragile molecule which the viral protein serves to protect, is much less particular. For example, poliomyelitis is primarily a disease of men, monkeys and chimpanzees, and it will not infect frogs; the protein of a polio virus cannot attach itself to the cells of a frog. However, if the protein is stripped away and the nucleic acid alone is placed on frog cells in a tissue culture, the frog cells become infected. They proceed to produce new polio viruses, and the particles that come out are complete with protein overcoats; they look just like the original polio viruses that furnished the nucleic acid.

It appears likely that within a few years we shall be able to infect plant cells with animal viruses or animal cells with plant viruses if we use only the nucleic acids.

NUCLEIC ACID was discovered almost a century ago in the nucleus of animal cells. However, it did not appear to have any special significance until 1944 when it was found to be the genetic material by which hereditary characteristics are transferred from parent to child. Today, we know that the specifications, the "blueprints," for each and every bit of life on earth is coded in the sequence of nucleotides which constitutes the nucleic acid molecule.

Nucleic acid, as we know, occurs in two different forms: DNA, which was discovered in human pus cells in 1865; and RNA, which was discovered in yeast about 30 years later.

DNA is found in every one of the 10,000,000,000,000 cells in the human body and in the cells of all other animals. It is peculiar to the chromosomes in the cell nucleus and is not found in any other part of the nucleus or anywhere else in the cell. It always occurs in the same amount in all the body cells of any one species of animal, regardless of whether the cells come from nerves, blood, bone or muscle. Egg and sperm cells contain only half the normal allotment.

DNA is incredibly thin, perhaps 12 atomic diameters across, but the strands of DNA in a single human cell would reach nearly six feet if stretched to full length. This amounts to some 10,000,000,000 miles of DNA in every man and woman alive.

Viruses, of course, are built around a core of nucleic acid; but there is considerable variation in the relative amounts of nucleic acid and protein. Nucleic acid accounts for one per cent, by weight, of the influenza virus, 25 per cent of the polio virus, and 50 per cent of the bacterial viruses. Bacterial viruses contain DNA, while such viruses as TMV, polio, mumps and influenza contain RNA.

The design of the nucleic acid molecule is remarkable for the efficiency it embodies and the versatility it permits. The molecule is extremely complex, and yet the general principle on which it is built is simple. The principle is that of polymerization, the linking together of a great many similar units; and the nucleic acid molecule is certainly a most elegant and sophisticated example of a polymer.

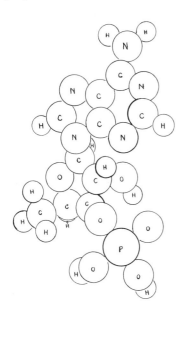

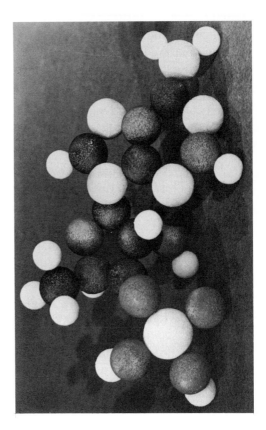

The basic unit of the molecule is the nucleotide, a precisely patterned arrangement of between 29 and 35 atoms. Only four different kinds of nucleotides occur in a nucleic acid molecule, although they are repeated many many times. Above is a model of the nucleotide, *adenylic acid*. Individual atoms are identified in the diagram.

A nucleotide is composed of three distinct groups of atoms: a base, a sugar and a phosphate group. The sugar and the phosphate are identical in all nucleotides throughout the entire length of a nucleic acid molecule; they are linked together, sugar-to-phosphate-to-sugar-to-phosphate, in a long, monotonous array, and they form the "backbone" to which the bases are attached. The base is the distinctive badge of the individual nucleotide.

Five bases are involved in making one or the other of the two types of nucleic acid: *uracil, guanine, cytosine, adenine* and *thymine*. The nucleotides corresponding to these five bases are *uridylic acid, guanylic acid* (illustrated on the opposite page), *cytidylic acid, adenylic acid,* and *thymidylic acid*.

The five nucleotides are illustrated schematically below.

The first four, containing the bases uracil, guanine, cytosine and adenine, are the nucleotides of which the RNA molecule is composed. The four on the right, containing the bases guanine, cytosine, adenine and thymine, are the DNA nucleotides. RNA does not contain thymine; DNA does not contain uracil.

There are two other major structural differences between RNA and DNA. The first is that each contains a different sugar. Therefore, the guanylic, cytidylic and adenylic acids of RNA are not the same as those of DNA.

The second difference is that RNA is a long, single strand of linked nucleotides whereas DNA is a double strand. There are probably one or more exceptions to this last statement, however, for a DNA molecule which appears to be single-stranded was isolated recently from the tiny bacterial virus, φX174.

base
(guanine)

sugar

phosphate

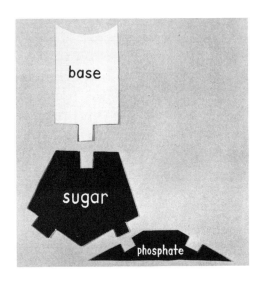

base

sugar

phosphate

DNA nucleotide
(deoxyguanylic acid)

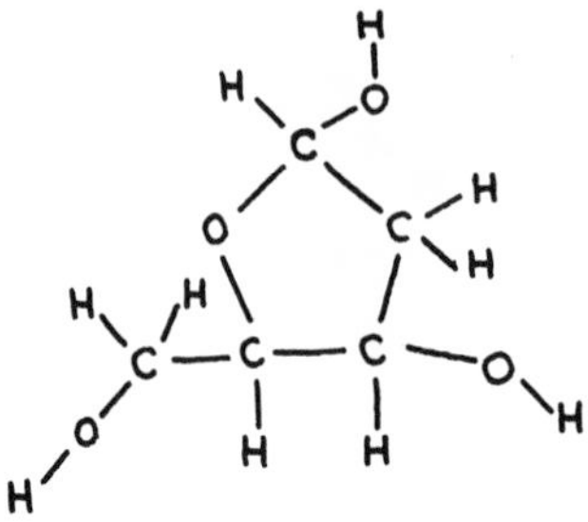

deoxyribose
$C^5 H^{10} O^4$

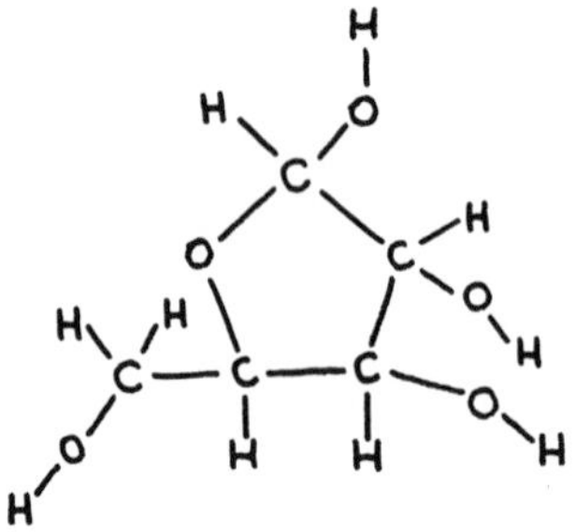

ribose
$C^5 H^{10} O^5$

The difference between the two sugars is the basis for the names *deoxyribonucleic acid* and *ribonucleic acid*. The RNA sugar, ribose, is a simple sugar containing five oxygen atoms in each molecule. Deoxyribose, as the prefix *de-oxy* suggests, is ribose with one particular oxygen atom removed.

RNA nucleotides combine, as illustrated on the opposite page, to form long RNA molecules. The model illustrates either a simple trinucleotide or three units of a much longer molecule like the RNA of tobacco mosaic virus. The three groups of white spheres represent bases and the black spheres represent the sugar-phosphate "backbone" of the molecule. The structural formula illustrates the same trinucleotide.

A schematic picture of a small fragment of a typical RNA molecule appears at the lower right.

There is no structural reason why RNA nucleotides cannot be joined together in random order, or even why, theoretically, a large RNA molecule could not consist entirely of one kind of nucleotide.

This is not the case with DNA, however. The bases of the DNA nucleotides are classified into two groups: the *pyrimidines*, cytosine

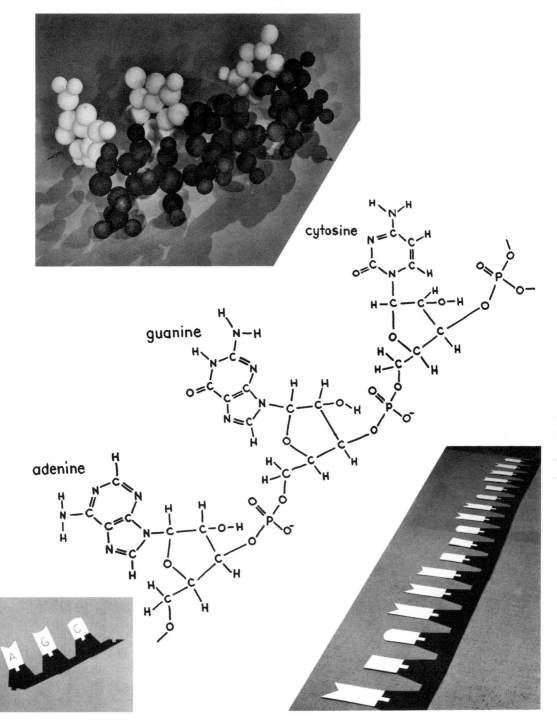

cytosine

guanine

adenine

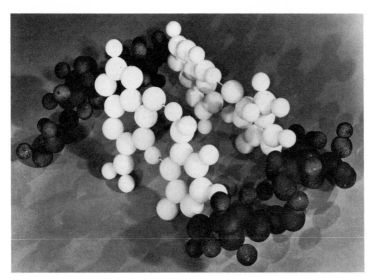

cytosine

guanine

thymine

adenine

and thymine; and the somewhat longer *purines*, guanine and adenine.

pyrimidines:	thymine	cytosine
purines:	adenine	guanine

DNA is a ladder-like molecule, a two-rung section of which is illustrated in the model opposite. Two parallel lines of repeating sugar-phosphates form the sides of the ladder, and a pair of bases forms each rung. The bases are joined by two relatively weak hydrogen bonds, indicated on the structural diagram by broken lines.

It is obvious that every rung must be the same length if the sides of the ladder are to remain at the same distance from one another. This would not be possible if one rung were formed by two purines and the next by two pyrimidines, which are shorter than purines; so every rung, that is, every base pair, must contain one purine and one pyrimidine.

However, a rung composed of adenine-cytosine or of guanine-thymine is impossible because no hydrogen bonds can be formed; the crucial hydrogen atoms are not in the right location.

The only possibility left is for adenine always to pair with thymine and for guanine always to pair with cytosine. And this is apparently what happens.

Consequently, the sequence of nucleotides on one side of the ladder always dictates the sequence on the other side. Whenever thymine occurs on one side, adenine *must* occur on the other.

The DNA "ladder" is actually twisted like a spiral staircase,

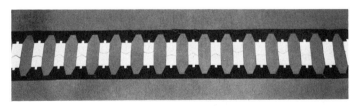

and its final form can be illustrated in the model on page 150.

The three-dimensional structure of this great molecule, with its double helix and its specifically mated base pairs, was deduced in 1952 by J. D. Watson and F. H. C. Crick. The principal evidence they had to work with was a series of X-ray diffraction pictures which reflected the many subtleties of DNA structure in an exceedingly indirect form.

Erwin Chargaff and others reported that the relative amounts of the four different bases appeared to be fixed for all animal species, irrespective of the individual or the organ from which the DNA was taken. The proportions usually differed for DNA taken from different species, but the differences between closely related species were small.

This similarity in composition among the DNA molecules of similar organisms reflects the significance of nucleic acid as the carrier of genetic information. The DNA in the cell of a jellyfish is vastly different from that in the cell of a gorilla. We assume that chimpanzee DNA, on the other hand, must be roughly similar to gorilla DNA, and that the DNA of two individual gorillas must be alike in all major respects.

Every nucleic acid molecule contains a specific list of chemical instructions written in a code that employs only four symbols—G, C, A, and either U or T. Although we do not know just how this information is encoded or communicated, we do know that the molecule is capable of carrying any one of an unlimited variety of messages. For example, the four nucleotides of a nucleic acid molecule only a few hundred units long can be arranged in so many different ways that every grain of sand in the Sahara could be represented by a different arrangement, with enough left over to label every star in the Milky Way.

In general, the number of nucleotides in each DNA molecule increases as we progress from simpler to more complex organisms. The single DNA molecule of the ϕX174 virus contains about 6,000 nucleotides, while the DNA of a bacterium contains about 5,000,000. Every human cell contains not one DNA molecule but about 800,000 of them, and each of these is composed of something like 40,000 nucleotides.

These observations about the structure of nucleic acid represent a very small sampling of a great reservoir of new knowledge—all of it accumulated within the past 15 years. Not often in the history of science has so much been learned so quickly.

On the other hand, the subject is so new and so vastly complex that our reservoir of knowledge looks quite meager at second glance. The most significant and the most intriguing aspects of our concentrated study of nucleic acid can be stated only in the form of questions yet to be answered.

How does nucleic acid manage to shape the destiny of the cell and, ultimately, of the whole organism of which it is so small a fragment? How does it relay the information it carries to distant regions of the cell? How is the information stored in the first place? What is the code? What structural differences in the molecule lead to what specific biological consequences? How, precisely, does nucleic acid go about making a perfect copy of itself?

These questions lead us beyond mere description of chemical structure; they lead us directly into the problems of chemical function.

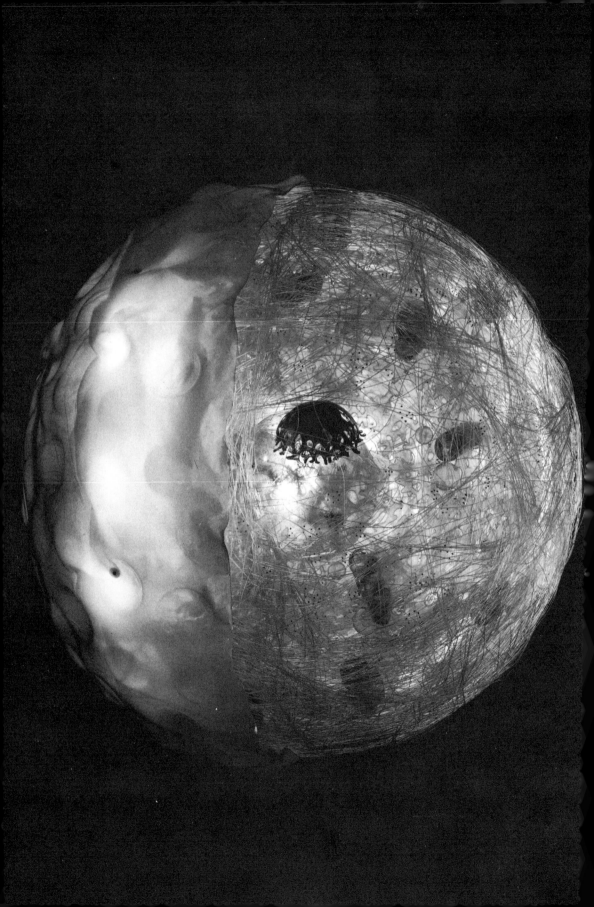

THE CHEMISTRY OF LIFE

How DNA Makes DNA

EVERY LIVING cell is a microcosm in which nucleic acid functions as a dictator—a benevolent one usually, but a sadistic despot in the case of cancer and a usurper of power in the case of a virus.

In any case, the nucleic acid is ultimately responsible for the 10,000 or more chemical reactions that occur in a cell every minute in the interests of maintaining or reproducing a great variety of specialized structures. The complexity of some of these structures is evident in this generalized model of a human body cell at a magnification of 10,000 diameters.

A central problem in biology has always been the question of how the cell manages to reproduce itself. How is the pattern of life passed on from generation to generation, in cells individually and in the precisely ordered aggregates of cells that constitute a living creature?

It has long been known that the answer to this question was to be found—if it could be found at all—in the chromosomes. The human chromosomes pictured here are roughly typical of these stubby, crooked structures found in the nucleus of every living cell. Various characteristics such as eye color or the number of toes on a foot are related to specific localized

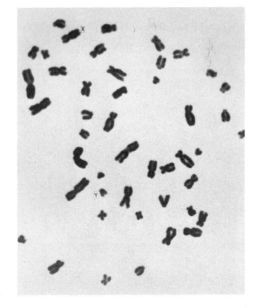

areas on a chromosome, called *genes;* the same is true for characteristics such as the ability or lack of ability of the cell to perform certain chemical functions.

But how do genes work and what are they made of?

George W. Beadle and Edward L. Tatum showed in 1941 that genes operate by controlling the production of enzymes which, in turn, control chemical reactions in the cell. And at this time it was thought that genes, like enzymes, were essentially proteins.

Meanwhile, a sticky material called *TP*, or "transforming principle," had been found in a particular type of pneumococcus, the bacterium which causes pneumonia. When this TP was injected into a second type of pneumococcus, it transformed the second type into the first type.

In 1944, Oswald T. Avery and his colleagues at the Rockefeller Institute purified TP and discovered that it was a constituent of chromosomes but was not a protein. TP was, in fact, DNA.

Genes, then, were obviously made of DNA plus protein.

This knowledge still offers no clue as to how chromosomes might duplicate themselves. But a likely answer suggests itself when we consider the structure of DNA as given by the Watson-Crick model. If the DNA can become uncoiled and if its paired strands begin to separate at one end, each nucleotide should be able to pick up an appropriate partner from unattached nucleotides in the medium. Since there is only one type of mate possible for each nucleotide, the two

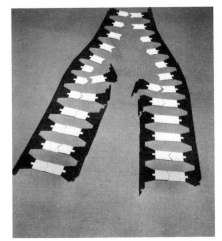

resulting DNA molecules will be identical with one another and with the original "parent" molecule. Each half of the parent has served as a template for the assembly of the other half.

Whatever the actual mechanics of duplication may be, nucleic acid can be assembled artificially in the laboratory. Arthur Kornberg succeeded in making synthetic DNA in 1957 while working at Washington University in St. Louis. Severo Ochoa of New York University synthesized RNA about the same time, and the two were awarded the Nobel Prize for medicine in 1959 for their separate accomplishments.

Dr. Kornberg, who is now at Stanford University, made DNA by adding to appropriate enzymes a mixture of unattached nucleotides plus a tiny amount of natural DNA which acted as a "primer," probably by serving as an initial template. The enzymes made it possible for the free nucleotides to join together as new molecules of DNA. The chemical events in Dr. Kornberg's experiment apparently simulated the way in which DNA is made in living cells. The new DNA was not biologically active, but it probably was a faithful copy of the DNA which Dr. Kornberg used as a primer.

DNA has also been produced without cellular enzymes, although the product was "nonsense" DNA, made with a random sequence of nucleotides which carried no meaningful information.

The fact that nucleic acid can be made synthetically suggests exciting prospects.

Theoretically, it might be possible to design and make a nucleic acid that would act as a "transforming principle": this "transforming principle" might be able to change the harmful characteristics of cancer cells just as the original "TP" altered the genetics of the pneumococcus.

It is also conceivable that a harmless nucleic acid could be made which would collect around it the protein of a dangerous virus; this laboratory virus then could be used as a vaccine since the protein would confer immunity while the nucleic acid remained inactive. It might even be possible to design a virus which would attack only cancer cells.

Such speculations are no longer rated as science fiction, but we are still a very long way from being able to synthesize a nucleic acid built to our own specifications.

It is possible that our first successful steps in this direction will involve the synthesis of extremely simple DNA chains which could substitute for genes in experimental situations. Recent studies indicate that a single gene may consist of a strand of DNA only a few hundred nucleotides in length. Furthermore, a change of only a single nucleotide may prove to be quite enough to cause the simplest genetic change, or mutation.

Meanwhile, we have a great deal more to learn about the nature of genetic change.

Ideally, we would like to study just one trait at a time, that is, one gene at a time. A scientist tries to design an experiment or discover a natural circumstance in which one element is changeable but everything else remains constant and stable. Then when this one variable element is altered he can be reasonably certain that any effects he observes are due to this one change.

Biologically, changes in one gene can be demonstrated; they happen spontaneously and sometimes they can be induced by irradiation or chemical treatment.

Such a mutation may result in the death of the cell, but in other cases some new cell characteristic may appear instead. Then, if the cell proceeds to divide normally, this new characteristic is handed down to all the cell's descendants.

This natural fact gives us, at least in theory, the chance to compare two chromosomes which differ only in a minor way. Here, it would seem, is an opportunity to discover precisely what differences exist in the chemical structure of these two chromosomes.

In the following two chapters, C. Arthur Knight and Heinz L. Fraenkel-Conrat investigate two different aspects of mutation among viruses. Dr. Knight—shown on the next page weighing a very large sample of tobacco mosaic virus—will discuss the subtle chemical differences between similar mutants. Dr. Fraenkel-Conrat will discuss the function and structure of nucleic acid in a virus.

The Chemistry of Mutation

It would be nice to study chemically the process of gene mutation in chromosomes, for we should very much like to know what kind of chemical change, if any, occurs in this key hereditary material.

However, such a study is just about hopeless in the case of most living things. In many-celled organisms, it takes a specialist just to *find* the chromosomes. They are so intimately involved with the hundreds of other cellular constituents that it becomes most difficult to isolate them.

What we need is a simple creature, an organism resembling a naked chromosome or resembling the functional subunit of the chromosome, which is usually called a "gene." In short, we need an organism which is made of nothing but protein and nucleic acid, which has no function other than that of reproducing itself, and which is subject to mutation.

Viruses come very close to having just such characteristics.

So we thought, why not study the chemistry of virus mutation?

To do this, we selected a common strain of tobacco mosaic virus and a mutant strain which produces different disease symptoms. Next, we inoculated a series of tobacco plants with each of these two strains. The infected plants showed the symptoms you see on the following page, those on the left for TMV, the common strain of tobacco mosaic virus, and those on the right for the mutant strain, which we call HR.

The TMV viruses were all direct descendants of the tobacco mosaic virus isolated and crystallized in 1935. The HR, or "Holmes ribgrass" viruses, were descendants of a strain found by Francis O. Holmes in an infected weed, ribgrass, which caught his eye as he was walking back from lunch in Princeton, N.J., one afternoon in 1940. It is

181

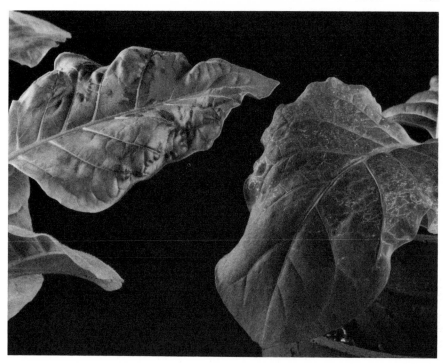

also a tobacco mosaic virus, but when distinguishing among different strains, the initials TMV are reserved for the common strain.

There is every reason to believe that the HR strain first occurred as a natural mutant of the common TMV strain at some time previous to its discovery. In fact, it had probably been subject to a number of different specific mutations at some time in the past.

The next part of our study was to isolate and purify the viruses from each of our two sets of diseased plants, and then to examine the individual virus particles to see if they might differ in any way in size and shape. As you can see in this electron micrograph, each of the three TMV particles appears to be identical with the two HR particles, and this relation holds when hundreds of particles are compared.

We made chemical and physical studies of about a thousandth of an ounce of each strain, and the results showed a very great structural similarity between them. Their over-all architecture seemed to be identical, with the same orderly, springlike array of some 2,200 subunits of protein arranged in a tall column, and the nucleic acid spiraling up on the inside.

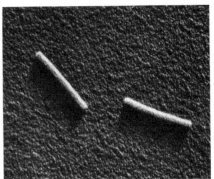

It became obvious that, if we were going to discover any difference at all between TMV and HR, it was to be found in the detailed chemical structure of the virus molecule.

By chemical means, we separated the outer protein coat from the nucleic acid core of each of the two strains, at the same time releasing the protein subunits from the virus superstructure. (Since the 2,200 subunits in any one virus particle are identical, we had 2,200 identical amino acid chains for every one of the billions of viruses in each of our two original preparations.)

To illustrate in schematic form the sort of difference which might occur between strain proteins, here is a very short section of what might represent TMV protein and a comparable section of what might be HR protein. The first, at the top, contains the possible amino acid sequence:

>proline–valine–cysteine–arginine–aspartic acid–
>proline–lysine–aspartic acid–phenylalanine–lysine

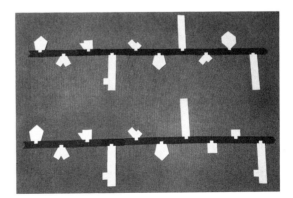

The second contains the sequence:

> proline—valine—cysteine—arginine—aspartic acid
> proline—lysine—serine—alanine—arginine

Note that these protein chains are the same except for the last three amino acids. Of course we did not yet know whether there were any differences of this kind between TMV and HR. The quickest way to find out how similar or different two long chains of protein are is to break them in a specific way and then compare the pieces. This we did by treating them with a digestive enzyme, trypsin, which is found in the digestive tract of human beings. Typically, trypsin causes the protein to come apart at the right-hand side of every arginine and lysine unit in the molecule, which in our examples would give these pieces:

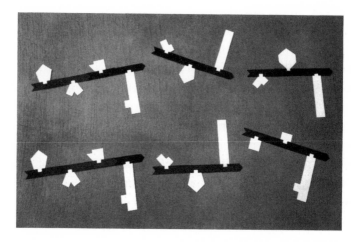

Now our task was to compare the short fragments of TMV protein with those of HR protein. If all the TMV fragments and all the HR fragments proved to be the same, then we would know that the two proteins were identical. If some fragments were the same and some different, we would know that TMV protein was not the same as HR protein. If all fragments differed, this would indicate that the two proteins were very different indeed.

In order to make the comparison, we had to use electrophoresis and chromatography to separate all the different HR fragments from one another, and then do the same for the TMV fragments.

First, we applied a portion of broken-up HR protein to a small area at the top of a large piece of damp filter paper. Then we subjected the paper to an electric current. Since many of the fragments differ slightly in their electric potential, they are drawn toward the positive or toward the negative side of the paper with varying force.

This gave us a partial separation of fragments, which were now spread in a line across the top of the paper.

But several different fragments may have essentially the same electric charges and would therefore bunch together, so chromatography was used to separate them. This consists of running a chemical solution—an organic solvent—down the sheet. Because the protein fragments differ from one another in the degree to which they will dissolve in the solvent, some fragments are carried farther down the paper than others.

The result was a piece of paper covered with spots, and this we call a map. Each spot is made by a collection of many thousands of identical protein fragments. In actual practice, we cannot see the spots until the end of the experiment; they are invisible until the paper can be dried and treated with a suitable coloring reagent.

We made a similar map for the TMV protein, and then compared the two maps.

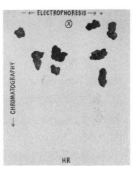

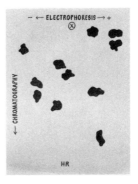

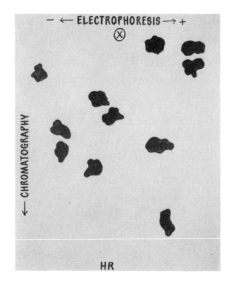

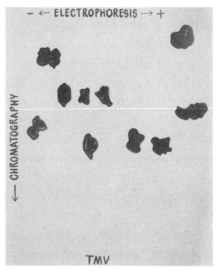

There were similar spots on both maps, indicating chemical similarities between the two viruses.

Much more exciting, however, was the discovery of different spots. For example, there is one spot in the upper right corner of the TMV map, but a whole cluster of spots in the comparable area on the map of HR; HR also has a distinctive spot at the lower right.

Clearly, we have here proof of a difference in the chemical make-up of TMV protein and HR protein.

We have made similar comparisons with virus strains even more closely related to TMV than is HR. In general, those separated from TMV by the fewest mutational steps are most similar in their protein compositions.

However, the most startling comparison was that of TMV and the "killer" strain, J14D1. TMV blisters and stunts young Turkish tobacco plants, but the plants continue to grow. J14D1 rapidly kills these same plants.

Chemical analysis showed that in the total of 158 amino acids comprising the protein subunits, J14D1 had one more lysine and one less glutamic acid than TMV. And, after tryptic digestion, the maps of the protein fragments of these two strains were found to be only slightly different.

This is a striking example of how small may be the chemical difference between the proteins of a mild strain of virus and a killer.

The same techniques of analysis have more recently been applied to the nucleic acid components of strains of tobacco mosaic virus. Again, significant differences have been found. These differences in the sequence of nucleotides—the building blocks of nucleic acid—appear to be the really vital differences between virus strains, because it has been found that the nucleic acid alone is sufficient to initiate an infection. Moreover, it is the nucleic acid that apparently dictates what kind of protein will be made during the reproduction of a virus inside a living cell. Thus the sequence of building blocks in the nucleic acid appears to provide a code which determines a specific sequence of amino acids in a long protein chain.

We have therefore been trying to go beyond mapping protein fragments and are attempting to analyze the complete sequence of amino acids in the virus proteins. In fact, we have just now—after many years of work—learned the order of the 158 amino acid units comprising the protein of TMV.

This has been a tedious project. Essentially, it involves breaking up the protein molecule with trypsin and with other enzymes which fracture the molecule at different points. Of particular value are enzymes which will kick loose single amino acid units one by one from the end of a protein fragment; this enables us to isolate the single amino acid residue from the rest of the fragment and identify it. When we have determined the sequence of amino acids in all of our fragments, we then try to fit this information together. This involves use of new enzymes which break the protein at different places. The sequences of these new pieces overlap those of the previous fragments and thus solve the riddle of their order in the complete chain.

As we are able to repeat the job with mutant virus strains, we shall be able to compare the viral proteins, building block by building block. Eventually, we may be able to do the same thing for the nucleic acid components, for it has already been done in part. This would bring us a step closer to the prospect of tearing the lethal stinger out of a virus by altering the virus chemically.

It is profitable to speculate about what such knowledge might have meant to the world in 1918. At that time, a new strain of influenza virus suddenly appeared, although no one then knew that flu was caused by a virus. Within a year and a half, the virus had killed some 20,000,000 people.

It now seems likely that the murderous character of this particular virus was simply an example of mutation in the relatively mild influenza virus familiar to man for hundreds of years. And we now suspect that this mutation involved only a small change in the structure of the common flu virus.

Of additional concern to us is the question of how our recent findings will apply to the much more complicated problem of gene mutation in chromosomes. We really can't answer this question yet, but there are tantalizing similarities between the structural subunit of the chromosome and the tobacco mosaic virus. Both—as we can see if we remove a few of the subunits from this idealized model of a

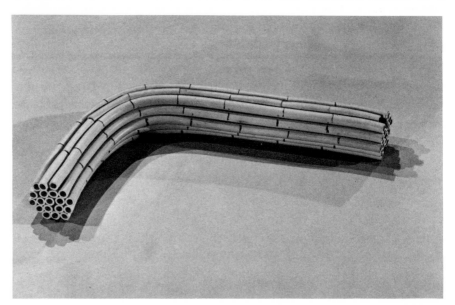

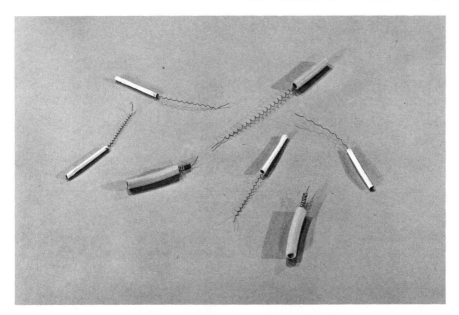

chromosome—can be represented as cylinders of characteristic protein surrounding a coiled thread of nucleic acid (DNA in the chromosome, RNA in TMV). Both, as we know, can duplicate themselves exactly and are subject to mutation.

We have already learned that mutation in viruses involves specific structural chemical changes in nucleic acid and protein. This is likely to be true also of chromosomes. And we now suspect that it should be theoretically possible to describe mutation and evolution, as well as reproduction, in terms of detailed chemical structure. In other words, the form and function of all "life" appear definable in terms of the way molecules are arranged in the chromosomes of living things.

C. ARTHUR KNIGHT

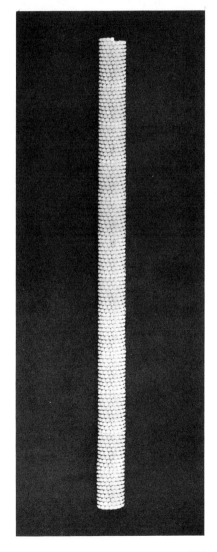

In order to study the function and structure of nucleic acid in a virus, we have first to choose a suitable virus with which to work. The venerable tobacco mosaic virus, commonly known as TMV, is the one we are going to investigate.

It is a rod-shaped virus 17 times as long as it is thick. The protein coat of this virus, as we know, consists of 2,200 small, separate protein units called peptide chains; they are arranged in a very orderly fashion, as you can see in this picture of a model of TMV, and they are all identical.

What we are interested in now, however, is the nucleic acid hidden inside the protein coat.

It is a long, threadlike molecule which runs through the entire length of the particle, coiling around some 130 times.

In a model of the virus, we can see the nucleic acid inside if we remove a few of the protein units. When the real nucleic acid is literally removed from the virus by

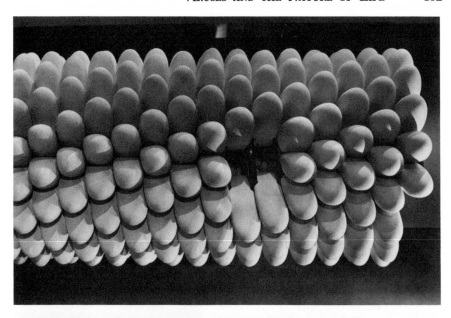

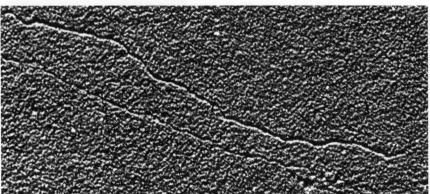

chemical means, it stretches out into a long, nearly straight thread, as shown in the electron micrograph.

The tobacco mosaic virus particle, then, is made of one long molecule of nucleic acid and 2,200 protein molecules. By weight, the protein constitutes 95 per cent of the virus. It is the remaining five per cent, the nucleic acid, which is of dominant importance.

This can be proved by separating the nucleic acid from the protein by chemical means and then applying the nucleic acid alone to a healthy tobacco leaf. The nucleic acid will proceed to cause disease in the tobacco plant in exactly the same way that the whole virus particle causes disease. If we apply only the viral protein to a healthy leaf, on the other hand, nothing happens.

The protein is far from useless, however. In terms of quantity, the nucleic acid alone is not nearly as efficient an infectious agent as the complete virus with its heavy protein overcoat. To cause disease, you have to put about 1,000 times as much nucleic acid on a leaf when the nucleic acid is not protected by the protein of the virus. It was first thought that this might be due to the fact that the chemist had inactivated the nucleic acid, harming it in the course of isolating it and separating it from the virus rod.

However, it soon became clear that this was not the reason. The reason that the nucleic acid alone is so very low in infectivity is that it is a very delicate chemical molecule. It is a long, stringlike molecule; as we know, it is composed of many units called nucleotides, 6,500 of them altogether to form the molecule in TMV.

These nucleotides are held together in the chain by phosphate-ester bonds which are very easily broken by chemical agents, particularly by the action of enzymes, and possibly even by mechanical forces. Enzymes attack the chain very readily and break the long thread into smaller pieces. And it has been clearly shown that only the entire length of the nucleic acid, the whole thread that goes from one end of the virus to the other, is infectious. If it is cut in two, it loses its infectivity.

It was therefore a very lucky discovery when we found that we could give back to an intact nucleic acid thread its original stability by putting it back into a protein coat. What we did was to carefully isolate protein units from the nucleic acid, and then—carefully so as to minimize breakage—isolate a sample of nucleic acid. It was found that, if the protein units were then brought together with the nucleic acid, the protein and nucleic acid would recombine to form, once again, a virus rod.

What apparently has happened, as illustrated on the following pages with models, is this: the tiny protein units undergo Brownian movement, being kicked around by the molecules of the fluid in which they are suspended. When the temperature of the fluid is high enough, the protein units collide with one another. Whenever two units strike one another in just the right position, they stick together.

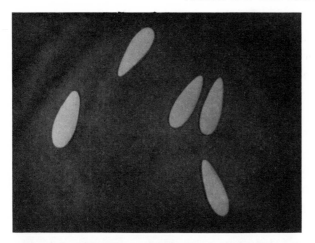

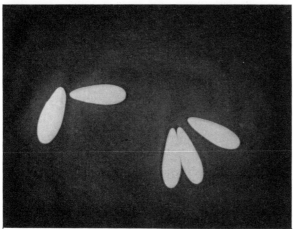

They have a great tendency to stick together whenever they happen to align themselves side by side, much like slices of pie in a pie tin. There must be molecular forces which connect and hold the units side by side in this way and which prevent them from sticking together in any other way. Now the nucleic acid comes into the picture. The protein units— seen singly or in pie-shaped groups— stick to the nucleic acid in a certain way as if they had grooves into which the nucleic acid could easily fit. The nucleic acid follows the pattern of the protein units and curls around to fit them. The protein units can never make one complete, flat circle. When a circle is nearly completed, there is not enough room left in the circle for another whole protein unit. Therefore, the addition of more units proceeds on top of the first ring of protein in the form of a spring, or helix. Actually, for each 360-degree turn of the nucleic acid there are just 16⅓ protein units.

Eventually, an entire new virus is built up with the nucleic acid helix deeply embedded within and the protein units evenly arrayed around it. The length of the finished virus is determined by the length of the nucleic acid molecule, and this molecule is always the same length in the case of the tobacco mosaic virus.

This complete process in which the isolated protein units and nucleic acid are brought to-

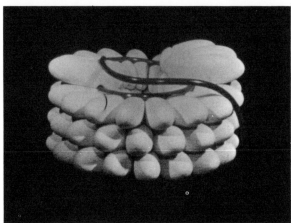

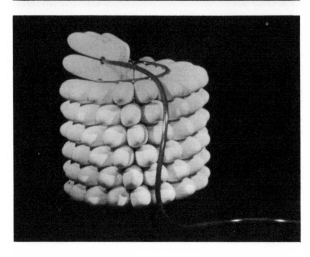

gether and allowed to construct new virus particles is called reconstitution. It is not a matter of "creating life in a test tube," as it has been labeled by a few anxious headline writers, but it is nevertheless a remarkable phenomenon. For it shows that the construction of a finished virus particle occurs automatically, requiring no enzymes and no mysterious "life force." One can literally take a virus apart and then put it back together again. And the new viruses that result can infect tobacco plants and reproduce themselves just as well as "natural" tobacco mosaic virus.

In all probability, the way in which these new viruses are formed in a test tube is not very different from the way in which viruses normally are formed inside the cells of the tobacco plant.

Now that we have seen how nucleic acid and protein manage to combine to form a complete virus particle, we are in a position to ask how we know that the nucleic acid is the more important of the two.

In our initial reconstitution experiment we allowed the nucleic acid from a given strain of virus to combine with the protein from others of the same strain.

But, sometime later, experiments were performed in which the nucleic acid from one strain of tobacco mosaic virus was combined with the protein of a different strain. This, we thought, would show clearly

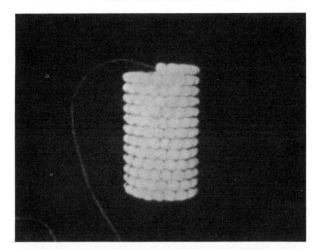

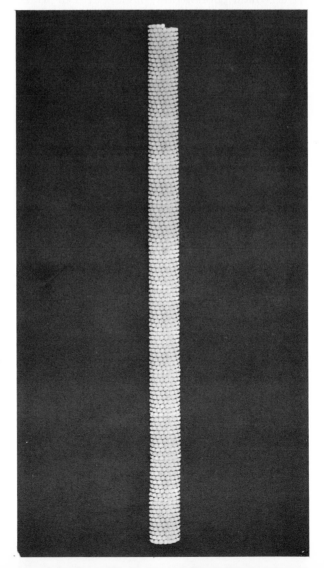

whether it is the nucleic acid or the protein that determines the genetic characteristics of a virus.

It is easy to distinguish different strains of a virus. One strain will be more virulent than another, or it will cause markedly different disease symptoms. In the case of influenza, for example, regular flu is quite distinct from Asian flu.

We took two different strains of tobacco mosaic virus—we'll call them strain A and strain B—and repeated our reconstitution experiment. We isolated the protein from the nucleic acid in strain A and did the same with strain B. Then we took just the protein from strain A and mixed it in a test tube with the nucleic acid from strain B. Reconstitution takes place, but we come out with a mixed virus which contains the nucleic acid of strain B coated with the protein of strain A.

Now, what will happen if we allow this mixed virus to infect a healthy tobacco leaf and reproduce within a leaf cell?

If the mixed virus is genetically stable, with both protein and nucleic acid contributing to its genetic properties, it should produce progeny viruses of the mixed-strain type. If the genetic or hereditary information of the virus resides in the protein, and not in the nucleic acid, then we should get progeny like the original A strain from which we obtained the protein for our mixed type. But if the genetic material of the virus is the nucleic acid rather than the protein, then we would expect the progeny to be like the original B strain from which the mixed virus obtained its nucleic acid.

What actually occurred was that we found all the progeny viruses to be pure strain B viruses. They caused the same disease symptoms in tobacco plants that the original strain B viruses caused.

So this experiment clearly showed us that the nucleic acid is boss and that it is the nucleic acid that determines the nature of the virus progeny from generation to generation. It maintains the identity of the virus even when we try to confuse it by wrapping the wrong kind of protein around it.

This experiment illustrates most forcefully that the nucleic acid, and not the protein, is the genetically active material, the genetically important part of the virus which determines the nature of the virus and the nature of the disease caused by the virus.

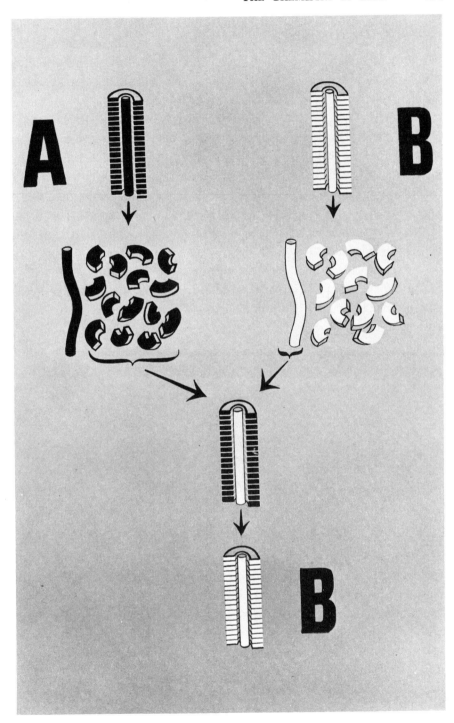

Now we come to a big question: how can the nucleic acid, a long, thin, threadlike molecule, possess such unique and specific biological activity? How can it carry and communicate all the information necessary to make new viruses of one and only one specific type? In some way, this tiny fiber must tell the tobacco leaf cell, "Make viruses exactly like the kind I came from originally, and do not make them with the protein of the type that I happen to be put together with by the chemists." This information, which the nucleic acid contributes to the cell it invades, is immensely detailed and specific.

The nucleic acid, as we know, is composed of nucleotides, single building units, of which there are four. The four types that occur in the tobacco mosaic virus are adenylic acid, guanylic acid, cytidylic acid and uridylic acid.

Each of these units can be represented as a block labeled with a letter—A, G, C, or U. There would be 6,500 of such blocks in the single molecule of the TMV nucleic acid. A short section of the molecule would look like this:

You can see very well that this is a code. The sequence AGUACUCAGUCGUCGCAGUCUCAAGU in our model is like a sentence or a paragraph in the submicroscopic language of nucleic acids. And a sequence of 6,500 letters obviously can carry a good bit of information. The fact that there are only four different symbols to work with—a four-letter alphabet—does not worry us much. The Morse code, after all, is composed only of three symbols, a dot, a dash, and a gap, and with this international three-letter alphabet you can write everything that has ever been written or will ever be written.

The practical question, of course, is: how can this information, carried in a very specific sequence of nucleotides, be translated? How can it be transformed into action on the part of an infected cell, into effects which lead to the production of an entirely new kind of material in the cell?

This question of how a chemical sequence can be translated into biological fact is the key problem facing biology in general at the moment.

Probably, almost certainly, nucleic acid functions by forcing the cell to make particular proteins, because everything that goes on in a cell is accomplished by enzymes, and enzymes are a variety of proteins.

It is known, for example, that the infection of a bacterium by a virus causes the production of completely new enzymes inside the bacterial cell, enzymes which the cell has never made before. Similarly, in other virus infections, new enzymes are produced which translate the commands of the nucleic acid—"Make this; make that; stop making the other"—into biochemical fact. Somehow, therefore, nucleic acid information is translated into protein information. Proteins are being manufactured at the command of the nucleic acid.

A protein, of course, can carry information about a particular job that must be done in much the same way that nucleic acid carries information, although no protein is known which carries instructions for its own reproduction. The protein molecule, of course, is also a very long chain composed of subunits, the amino acids.

Each of the 20 amino acids can be represented as a white block

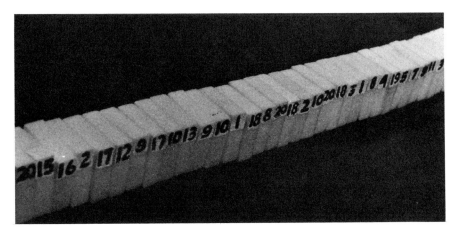

labeled with a number. And in this case we have a 20-letter alphabet instead of the four-letter alphabet of nucleic acid.

Each of the 2,200 units of protein in the tobacco mosaic virus is identical, and each consists of a coiled-up string of just 158 amino acids. There are only 16 of the 20 different kinds of amino acids in the protein of TMV, and the various numbers of each kind total 158.

Our problem is: how do we translate a language of four symbols into a language of 16 to 20 symbols? How can the four-letter code of nucleic acid be converted into a 20-letter protein code?

Various hypotheses have been suggested, although none of them has been proven definitely right and none of them represents the final word. But here is one theory which is easy to illustrate and which is as likely to be correct as any other that we could now show.

If we group the nucleotides into triads—GAU, UUG, AUC, for example—then each triad can represent one amino acid. GAU might represent leucine, UUG might represent glycine, and so forth.

Here is an example of the kind of translation that could be made:

leucine	glycine	alanine	leucine	proline	threonine
GAU	UUG	AUC	GAU	GAC	ACC

This, then, is a speculative idea of how a simple group of three nucleotides might determine a particular amino acid. Now you can see that a string of 6,500 nucleotides should be able to dictate the manufacture of a number of particular proteins, each with a unique sequence of amino acids. One of these proteins might be an enzyme necessary for the production of more nucleic acid; another might be the protein which ultimately will cover the nucleic acid and form a new virus particle.

Recently it has been possible to alter chemically the nature of a nucleotide. Several reactions have been studied by which we can do this. One case is particularly dramatic and exciting, partly because it is in a way the simplest. It simply amounts to replacing one amino group ($-NH_2$) by a hydroxyl group ($-OH$).

Here is a diagram of the structure of two of the four nucleotides found in the nucleic acid of TMV—cytosine and uracil.

cytosine   uracil

The amino group in the cytosine and the hydroxyl group in the uracil are shown at the top.

By using a chemical reagent, nitrous acid, we can knock the amino group off of cytosine, and replace it by a hydroxyl group. $-NH_2$ has been replaced by $-OH$.

The result? We no longer have cytosine but *uracil.*

This is a very exciting reaction. We have changed one nucleotide of the original molecule into another nucleotide which also does occur in the same molecule. We have turned cytosine into uracil.

Now suppose we apply a very small amount of nitrous acid to a TMV nucleic acid molecule. When this is done very cautiously, as few as one or two substitutions of C by U can be produced in the molecule.

Among the 6,500 nucleotides of which this molecule is made, we are likely to find the particular triad, GAC. The nitrous acid changes the C of this triad—the cytosine—into a U—uracil.

Suddenly the triad is no longer GAC but GAU. Therefore, when we translate this triad into its protein equivalent, according to our theoretical "dictionary," we no longer have the amino acid, proline; we have leucine instead, since GAU is the code for leucine.

So, by changing the identity of one nucleotide, we have managed to dictate the manufacture of a protein containing leucine at a point where proline normally would have occurred.

In other words, a mutant strain of virus has been produced.

I mention this particular case because this is just what occurred in a recent experiment in our laboratory. We isolated the nucleic acid of a virus and treated it with nitrous acid. Then we allowed the altered nucleic acid to build a new protein coat. The original nitrous acid experiments were carried out by H. Schuster, G. Schramm, A. Gierer, K. W. Mundry and others in Tübingen, Germany.

Actually, it is not easy to produce a mutant in which only one of the 6,500 nucleotides is changed, and the one we particularly focused our attention upon was one in which there were about four changes in the whole chain of 6,500 nucleotides. We have studied a great variety of mutants produced by such chemical changes, but this one was convenient to isolate and study.

It turned out that the protein coat of this mutant was different from the protein of the original parent virus.

This was not inevitable, because the nucleic acid is a very long thread and it determines more than the making of a protein coat. For example, it commands the cell to make certain enzymes, and this was not an enzyme but just coat protein.

But when we studied the protein coat of a particle changed in this manner, we found that several of the amino acids which constitute the protein had been changed. To be exact, there were three. Three amino acids out of the 158 had been replaced by three others.

One of the replacements was that of proline by leucine.

Now what difference could this change make to the virus?

The sequence of 158 amino acids which makes up the virus protein is now well established (see page 212), and we know that there is a proline near the outer end of each protein unit; that is, near the surface of the virus rod. We also know that the presence of proline in this position makes the virus more resistant to plant enzymes which might otherwise inactivate the virus.

So we can see that, by causing a minute chemical change in the nucleic acid of a virus, we have created a new strain of viruses which is distinctly less stable than was the parent strain.

And it may be that the chemical change which leads to a new strain of polio or flu is just as simple—perhaps just one nucleotide out of 6,500 accidentally replacing another. The fact that each infecting molecule represents the blueprint for its own reproduction makes each mistake, accident or deliberate chemical alteration a potentially immortal event.

The chemical production of a mutant plant virus, however, is only the very beginning of a lot of work that is before us. We are taking the first small steps. We are beginning to unravel the code that relates protein structure to the structure of nucleic acid.

Gradually, in the course of many years, the way in which genetic information is transferred will become clear. Gradually, also, the mechanism by which enzymes operate within a cell is being clarified by many workers in the field of biochemistry.

When this work on genetic information and the work on enzyme function is put together, our children—or our grandchildren, probably —will begin to have a clear understanding of the highly organized interplay of enzymes and genetic material, of energy and blueprints, which we call life.

HEINZ L. FRAENKEL-CONRAT

The Thread of Life

THE FIRST thing to be known about the structure of viruses was that they were made of protein. Later they were found to contain nucleic acid as well.

Likewise, the first thing to be known about the composition of genes and chromosomes was that they were essentially proteins; only later did we appreciate the fact that they were *nucleo*proteins.

The findings of Drs. Gierer and Schramm in Tübingen and of Dr. Fraenkel-Conrat in Berkeley provide convincing evidence of a direct, causative relationship between specific nucleic acid and specific protein synthesis; and this makes it possible to consider the action of both virus and gene in terms not of nucleoprotein structure but simply in terms of nucleic acid structure.

We have discovered an intimate relationship to exist between viruses and some cancer cells. We have also found that the action of genes is responsible for abnormal development in cancer as well as for normal growth, reproduction and mutation.

We can see that viruses, cancer, genes and life are all directly dependent upon the structure of nucleic acid. Both literally and figuratively, nucleic acid proves to be the thread of life.

Fundamentally, life in all its forms derives from the arrangement of four nucleotides in nucleic acid molecules which, in turn, determine the arrangement of 20 amino acids in molecules of protein.

This is one of the great discoveries of our century. It has transformed the science of biology and established the science of virology. No scientist today can study cancer or heredity or viruses without becoming deeply involved in the study of the other two as well.

Viruses, cancer, genes, and questions concerning the nature and origin of life are tied together by a whole series of interrelationships. Viruses can act as genes and genes can act as viruses under certain circumstances. Viruses can cause cancer and, within limits, can destroy cancerous tissue.

Furthermore, viruses offer us a unique key to understanding the function of nucleic acid, and perhaps, therefore, to understanding the nature of life itself. Viruses are relatively simple. They are the only objects from which we can remove the stuff of life—nucleic acid— and purify it, chemically modify it, put it back in the cell, and still have it biologically active. The progeny viruses subsequently can be recovered from the cell for all kinds of study.

Viruses may prove to be of utmost importance to scientists because they provide an approach to the study of evolution—the process by means of which all life on earth has developed.

We have recently come to appreciate the fact that evolution must have begun a billion or more years before any form of life appeared on earth. The earth's atmosphere some three billion years ago probably consisted of simple molecules such as hydrogen (H_2), water (H_2O), methane (CH_4), ammonia (NH_3), and perhaps carbon dioxide (CO_2). Chemical evolution must have begun with the conversion of these simple substances into more complex molecules by means of heat, ultraviolet light, cosmic rays, lightning or other natural sources of energy.

Water, methane, ammonia, and carbon dioxide are made from the elements hydrogen, carbon, oxygen and nitrogen. These four elements —the principal elements of which viruses and all living creatures are composed—are among the five most abundant elements in the universe. (Helium, the second most abundant element after hydrogen, is chemically inactive.)

Molecules made from these four elements must have accounted for much of the condensed matter of the universe at one time or another. In fact, Melvin Calvin of the Lawrence Radiation Laboratory at the University of California has found evidence of molecules similar to cytosine—a component of nucleic acid—in meteorites from space.

In experiments designed to test various theories of chemical evolution, radiation has succeeded in producing the following series of chemical transformations:

carbon dioxide and water into formic acid (H—CO—OH)
formic acid and water into acetic acid (CH₂—CO—OH)
acetic acid into succinic acid (OH—CO—CH₂—CH₂—CO—OH)

So we know that a four-carbon compound can be created from chemicals in a primitive atmosphere by the influence of radiant energy alone.

In another experiment, Stanley L. Miller at the University of Chicago created simple amino acids (glycine and alanine) by bombarding with electrical discharges similar to lightning the same kind of primitive atmosphere (water, methane, ammonia, and carbon dioxide).

Glycine, produced by electrical discharge, and succinic acid, produced by irradiation, can in turn be converted by natural processes into more complex molecules which are closely related to natural proteins; and individual amino acids can be converted into polypeptide chains under the influence of heat.

Furthermore, glycine, succinic acid, formic acid and carbon dioxide can combine naturally to form thymine, adenine, cytosine, and guanine—the all-important bases of which DNA is made.

We see, then, that both protein and nucleic acid can be formed naturally from some half dozen chemicals existing in a primitive atmosphere. However, the purely random processes which lead to the formation of more and more complex molecules also lead, even more readily, to the destruction of complex molecules. Nevertheless, some large molecules persist because their chemical activity favors the production of more of the same kind of molecules; that is, they act as catalysts, or enzymes, which speed up the rate of their own production.

Molecules of every sort are constantly mixing and colliding everywhere on earth. Each particle collides many times every second, and its specific structure allows it to combine occasionally with some other particle in a particular way. Even though few collisions result in promising new combinations, the number of molecular events on earth in a billion years is so great that the emergence of life seems to have been inevitable, given the initial starting conditions. Current knowledge also suggests that living forms must have evolved on some 100,000,000 other planets in the universe.

The evolution of higher forms of life undoubtedly depends upon the chemical evolution of a structure like nucleic acid which has the ability to reproduce itself and to preserve all the information necessary for the fabrication of such a complex organism as man.

The study of viruses enables us to investigate in detail the structure and function of nucleic acid, and thus to make some educated guesses as to how life began and evolved on earth.

Today, we are not too far from being able to learn the sequence of nucleotides in nucleic acid and the characteristics of living things which are determined by particular sequences. There is also the eventual prospect of being able to effect deliberate mutations and possibly of being able to control some significant characteristics of living things.

There is even hope that one day we might be able to make synthetic viruses designed to attack selected organisms, including, possibly, cancerous cells. Already, cancer researchers are making "fraudulent" nucleotides in an attempt to sabotage the function of DNA in cancer cells. And virologists are considering the possibility of making vaccines by "replating" harmless nucleic acid with the "wolves' clothing" of dangerous viruses.

Eventually, chemists should be able to synthesize a small nucleic acid molecule with its nucleotides arranged in a specific, predetermined order. Hence, it is not impossible that a structure possessing genetic continuity may be created artificially.

In the long run, we shall probably succeed in determining the detailed structure of nucleic acid and of genetically related protein; and we can investigate how the two are related structurally. With luck, we should be able to learn how to put together the building blocks of both nucleic acid and protein. *Then* we would be in a position to make viruses, or at least the nucleic acid of viruses.

Such an accomplishment could be considered as the artificial creation of a simple form of life.

APPENDIX

TMV Protein

THE COMPLETE amino acid sequence of the protein of the tobacco mosaic virus was announced by the University of California Virus Laboratory in November, 1960.

TMV protein is the largest protein for which the complete amino acid sequence has been determined. The string of 158 amino acids on the opposite page represents the polypeptide chain which, when coiled up and folded over on itself, comprises each of TMV's 2,200 protein subunits.

The 16 amino acids of TMV (and their three-letter abbreviations) are listed below in order of their respective frequencies in the protein. The number represents the number of times the particular amino acid residue occurs.

18	Asp	Aspartic acid
16	Glu	Glutamic acid
16	Ser	Serine
16	Thr	Threonine
14	Ala	Alanine
14	Val	Valine
12	Leu	Leucine
11	Arg	Arginine
9	Ileu	Isoleucine
8	Pro	Proline
8	Phe	Phenylalanine
6	Gly	Glycine
4	Tyr	Tyrosine
3	Try	Tryptophan
2	Lys	Lysine
1	Cys	Cysteine

158

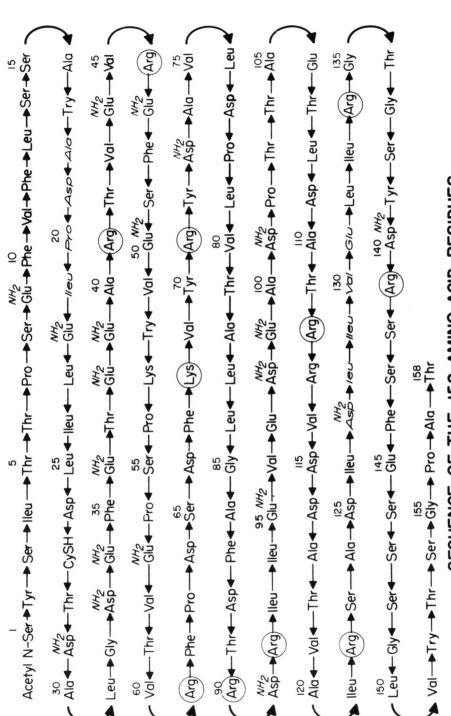

SEQUENCE OF THE 158 AMINO ACID RESIDUES
IN THE PROTEIN SUBUNIT OF TOBACCO MOSAIC VIRUS

VIRUS LABORATORY, UNIVERSITY OF CALIFORNIA AT BERKELEY

GUEST AUTHORS

THE SIX signed chapters in this book were written by the following members of the Senior Staff of the University of California Virus Laboratory in Berkeley, California.

The University's Virus and Biochemistry Laboratory is shown on the facing page.

HEINZ L. FRAENKEL-CONRAT, Professor of Virology in the Department of Virology, and Research Virologist to the Virus Laboratory. Doctor Fraenkel-Conrat received the California Scientist of the Year Award for 1958 for his discovery of infectious nucleic acid from tobacco mosaic virus. He received nationwide acclaim in 1955 for his reconstitution of an active virus from inactive parts of a virus and in 1960 for his demonstration that a specific change in the nucleic acid of a virus could result in a specific, inheritable change in the protein structure of the virus.

C. ARTHUR KNIGHT, Professor of Virology, Professor of Biochemistry, and Research Biochemist to the Virus Laboratory. Doctor Knight, who was associated with the Rockefeller Institute for Medical Research in Princeton for eight years before coming to the University of California, is particularly interested in the chemical relationships between viral strains and between host and virus.

ARTHUR B. PARDEE, Associate Professor of Virology, Associate Professor of Biochemistry, and Associate Research Biochemist to the Virus Laboratory. Doctor Pardee's special interest is in the nature and formation of enzymes and the effects of virus infection on metabolism. In 1960 he received the Paul-Lewis Laboratories Award in enzyme chemistry.

HARRY RUBIN, Professor of Virology and Research Virologist to the Virus Laboratory. Doctor Rubin is Associate Editor of *Virology*, and his research interests are concerned with the interaction between tumor viruses and individual animal cells. In 1958 he received the Anne Frankel-Rosenthal Cancer Research Award of the American Association for the Advancement of Science for his contributions to the un-

derstanding of the quantitative biological aspects of the relations between tumor viruses and animal cells.

GUNTHER S. STENT, Professor of Virology, Professor of Bacteriology, and Research Biochemist to the Virus Laboratory. Doctor Stent spent the year 1950-51 at the Institute of Cytophysiology of the University of Copenhagen and the year 1951-52 at the Pasteur Institute of Paris as an American Cancer Society Fellow. His research interests are concerned with bacterial viruses, particularly the study of their reproduction and their genetics.

ROBLEY C. WILLIAMS, Professor of Virology, Research Biophysicist to the Virus Laboratory and Associate Director of the Virus Laboratory. Doctor Williams, formerly Professor of Physics at the University of Michigan, is past president of the Electron Microscope Society of America and currently president of the Biophysical Society. He is now a Special Consultant to the U. S. Public Health Service and to the U. S. Army. His particular interest is in the development of electron microscopy for the study of biological structures, and he is known for his work in developing the techniques of shadow-casting, quantitative assay of virus particles and freeze-drying.

Photograph Credits

Jacket	Robley C. Williams and Kenneth M. Smith
4, 9	Richard M. Fowler
5	Louis H. Yates
12	R. L. Steere
13	UCVL *
14	F. L. Schaffer, C. E. Schwerdt and R. L. Steere
15, 16	Models: KQED staff; photographs: R. M. Fowler
17	R. C. Williams
19	above, E. G. Valens; below, R. M. Fowler
20	above, E. G. Valens; below, UCVL
21	UCVL
22	R. C. Williams and C. Arthur Knight, UCVL
25	Wendell M. Stanley, UCVL
26	R. M. Fowler
27	UCVL
30	Kenneth M. Smith, Cambridge University
31	M. Demerec and V. Fano, Carnegie Institution of Washington
38	Model: John Ernest, London; composite photograph: R. M. Fowler
42-45	R. M. Fowler
46	Davidson Films, San Francisco
47-54	R. M. Fowler
55	UCVL
56, 57	R. M. Fowler
59	Rogert G. Hart, UCVL: below, UCVL
61	R. C. Williams and K. M. Smith
64	R. M. Fowler
66	Carl T. Mattern and Herman DuBuy, National Institutes of Health, Bethesda, Maryland

* University of California Virus Laboratory.

FOR FURTHER READING

Anfinsen, Christian B. *The Molecular Basis of Evolution*. New York: John Wiley & Sons, Inc., 1959.

Bernal, John D. *The Physical Basis of Life*. London: Routledge & Kegan Paul, Ltd., 1951.

Burnet, Frank M. *Viruses and Man* (2nd ed.). Baltimore, Md.: Penguin Books, 1955.

———, and Stanley, Wendell M. (eds.). *The Viruses*. 3 vols. New York: Academic Press, Inc., 1959. (For more advanced reading.)

Butler, John A. V. *Inside the Living Cell; Some Secrets of Life*. London: George Allen & Unwin, Ltd., 1959.

Cook, J. Gordon. *Viruses in the Cell*. London: George H. Harrap & Co., Ltd., 1956.

Dalldorf, Gilbert. *Introduction to Virology*. Springfield, Ill.: Charles C. Thomas, 1955.

Fox, Sidney W., and Foster, Joseph F. *Introduction to Protein Chemistry*. New York: John Wiley & Sons, Inc., 1957.

Fraenkel-Conrat, Heinz L. *Structure and Function at the Threshold of Life* (tentative title). New York: Academic Press, Inc., 1961.

Ginger, Ray (ed.). *Spectrum—the World of Science*. New York: Henry Holt & Co., 1959.

Luria, Salvador E. *General Virology*. New York: John Wiley & Sons, Inc., 1953.

The Physics and Chemistry of Life, a *Scientific American* Book. New York: Simon & Schuster, 1955.

Rivers, Thomas M. *Viral and Rickettsial Infections of Man* (3rd ed.). Edited by the author and Frank L. Horsfall, Jr. Philadelphia: J. B. Lippincott, 1959.

Scientific American Reader. New York: Simon & Schuster, 1953.

Smith, Kenneth M. *Beyond the Microscope* (Rev. ed.). Baltimore, Md.: Penguin Books, 1957.

Weidel, Wolfhard. *Virus*. Translated by Lotte Streisinger. Ann Arbor, Mich.: University of Michigan Press, 1959.

Williams, Greer. *Virus Hunters*. New York: Alfred A. Knopf, Inc., 1959.

The page numbers in *italic* indicate definitions or the most important references.